Stay Salty:

Life in the Garden State

A New Jersey
Anthology

Published by

Read Often. Read Well.

Published by Read Furiously. First Edition.

ISBN: 978-1-7371758-4-1

Anthology
Short Stories
Poetry
Comics
Photography
New Jersey

For more information on *Stay Salty: Life in the Garden State* or Read Furiously, please visit readfuriously.com. For inquiries, please contact samantha@readfuriously.com.

Edited by Samantha Atzeni and Adam Wilson

Read (v): The act of interpreting and understanding the written word.

Furiously (adv): To engage in an activity with passion and excitement.

**Read Often. Read Well.
Read Furiously!**

Table of Contents

Salt in the Game
by Samantha Atzeni ●

When I was growing up in Hudson County, my town and the New York City skyline were the only factors in my very small world. As I grew older, I recognized that the magic of New Jersey belongs to those who dare to venture outside their designated space: North Jersey, South Jersey, and the mythological universe known as Central New Jersey. Every area has its own positives and negatives, its own quirks and styles, and its own visual landscape. Traveling in New Jersey is unlike any other traveling experience. And I say this as someone who walked through a dense forest in Poland trying to find a bus station. Even today, I maintain that my ability to adapt in various areas and climates comes from my years as a New Jersey resident.

Children from New Jersey are taught very specific pieces of information about their state. There's the standard memorization of the state bird and flower (the eastern goldfinch and common meadow violet), the number of counties (21), and the state's status as a peninsula. Count 'em: on the eastern side, we have the Hudson River, the Upper and Lower New York Bays, the Kill Van Kull (a strait tucked comfortably between Bayonne and New York), and the big one, the Atlantic Ocean. The southern part brings us to Delaware Bay. Finally, the west side contains the Delaware River.

However, there are other, more telling pieces of information that only NJ children understand: their exit number, whether or not they like pork roll or Taylor ham, how to spot the best pizza IN THE WORLD (spoiler alert: pretty much anywhere in NJ), and how to navigate various forms of environmental backdrops - the ridges, the beaches, the farms, the cities, the main streets, the college towns, the pine forests, the cranberry bogs, the salt marshes...you get the idea.

Did you know that New Jersey has an official state dinosaur? It's the Hadrosaurus foulkii and his name is Haddy.

Our state vegetable is the tomato, but we also boast the best blueberries.

Overall, NJ kids are pretty smart - and I'm not just saying that because they know how to navigate a traffic circle from their carseats. But they do.

Our first volume, *The World Takes*, came from a very earnest place. We wanted to celebrate the state that allowed us to grow and flourish within its peninsula (I'm making my fourth-grade teachers very proud right now). We chose the phrase "the world takes" because Read Furiously is based in the Trenton area and Trenton does indeed make for the world to take.

At the time of this writing, Trenton also makes Olympians. Athing Mu, you are amazing. We celebrate you, your hometown of Trenton, and your Olympic gold medal!

The World Takes received a lot of wonderful submissions and when it hit shelves, we were met with a mixture of confusion, incredulity, and intrigue. "An entire book about NJ?" people asked us. But those who know New Jersey share our joy.

Yes, an entire book about New Jersey.

Yes, an entire book about the weird and wonderful people within it.

Yes, an entire book about the traffic, the food, the personalities, the places, and the weather.

Yes, an entire book about a way of life that is only understood and valued by those who have lived it.

With this new volume, we wanted to shift the focus to encapsulate a very distinct New Jersey personality: salt. The saltiness is all around us: from the Atlantic Ocean to the delicious taffy that we all buy too much of but still attempt to eat it all as summer fades into fall.

Legend has it that, in 1883, salt water taffy had been created when David Bradley, a local Atlantic City merchant, discovered a hurricane flooded the boardwalk, including his candy store. A young woman asked Bradley if the store was still open and if he was still selling his taffy. In an attempt at a joke, Bradley is believed to have answered that she could help herself to some "salt water taffy." Bradley's mother overheard them and the rest, as we like to say, is history. By the 1920's, salt water taffy became a beautifully packaged commodity that symbolizes a tasty end to a wonderful beach vacation. To me, a trip down the Shore synonymous with salt water taffy.

As with the stories of Jimmie Leeds, Hoppie the Sussex Sea Serpent, and Captain Kidd, I'm not sure how much of David Bradley's salt water taffy story is true. But storytelling is as much a part of New Jersey as the salt air, the boardwalk, the farm stands, and, of course, the taffy. Even as an urban legend from 1883, we see New Jersey residents coming back from a hurricane, disastrous flooding, and the complications of running a small business using their grit and humor (that NJ sarcasm we know and love) to move forward. Saltiness isn't just a piece of candy or a day at the beach.

In New Jersey, salt and its grit are a way of life. It's in those who don't care much for others' opinions and in those who have been through too much for those opinions to matter. It's in those who work really hard all the time, in those that hustle to keep moving forward. It's in the legacies and the lore. Many try to define saltiness as being "aggressive," but we see it as "of the Earth." That coarseness that makes dreams happen, raises families, bounces back from personal hardships, and pushes past when disasters of all kinds threaten to pull us down.

The pieces in *Stay Salty* capture the perfect New Jersey narrative - we have a mix of poetry, photography, comics, fiction and nonfiction. With every New Jersey anthology, we strive to capture all of the elements that make up this state and its residents. In creating this new volume, we were overwhelmed and grateful for the many submissions that we received. This new project confirmed something we already knew but love to keep hearing: you like New Jersey, you *really like* New Jersey.

This book is for those who are reading this because they are lucky enough to live in New Jersey and for those who wish they could be as cool as people from New Jersey.

May this book remind you that salt has the same texture as grit. May this book remind you of the strength that runs through New Jersey.

Hey, saltiness got us this far. Let's see what else it can do.

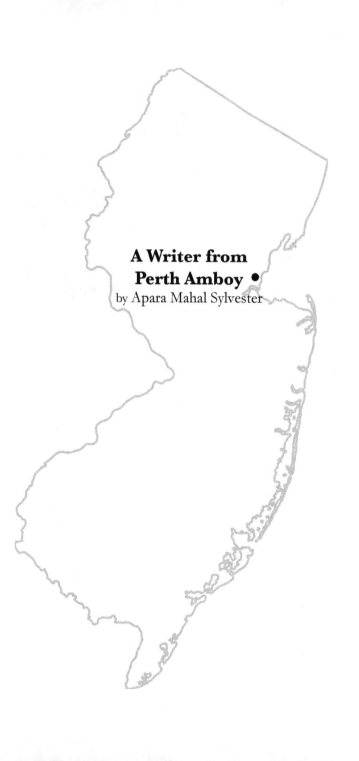

A Writer from
Perth Amboy ●
by Apara Mahal Sylvester

I have lived in New Jersey almost all of my life. I'm proud to call Perth Amboy my hometown. Located in Middlesex County, Perth Amboy has most notably a spectacular waterfront with grand old houses facing the Raritan Bay. It is also home to the oldest functioning city hall in the United States, which is listed on the New Jersey Register of Historic Places. It's a diverse city where every prism of culture can be found.

Though I moved out of Perth Amboy many years ago, I enjoy taking friends for a ride, telling them "I'm going to take you someplace special." I then proceed to drive them to the Perth Amboy waterfront, where they are always in awe of its beauty. After watching the sparkling calm waters, the bobbing boats, and viewing Staten Island on the other side, we usually end up having a drink at the Armory restaurant on the Bay, which is a restored naval ammunition building once used during World Wars I and II. We may also stop at The Barge restaurant for the best seafood Perth Amboy has to offer, or maybe even have afternoon tea and a tour of the Proprietary House, which is the only remaining official royal governor's mansion still standing in the original thirteen colonies.

I became an author long after I had moved out of Perth Amboy, but it was Perth Amboy where my writing spark was ignited. From an early age I used to like to "play type" on the typewriter. Looking back, perhaps this was a foreshadowing of what was to come.

Up until I was ten years old, my parents and I lived with my grandparents on Mary Street, which is towards the outskirts of town. I was the only child among many adults, and I was quite mature beyond my years. My first introduction to writing happened right on Mary Street, where I met one of my dearest childhood friends, a woman who lived a few houses down from my grandparents, and a writer.

Mary Book Farmer, or Mrs. Farmer as I called her, was a lifelong Perth Amboy resident and a columnist for the local newspaper. She wrote a weekly column titled "Glowing with Age." I would go to visit her house almost daily and she would always warmly welcome me inside. One of my fondest memories of Mrs. Farmer is taking her dog Harry for a walk to a beautiful old cemetery in our town, Alpine Cemetery. It was built on a lush rolling hillside. It was peaceful and quiet. I enjoyed our serene strolls.

When I was in my late teens, Mrs. Farmer retired and moved to Florida. We wrote letters for a while but then lost touch. She was a lovely, kind-hearted woman who accepted a little girl decades younger than her as her friend and invited her into her world. Somehow, her knack for writing must have rubbed off on me during our many walks.

I attended Most Holy Rosary School, one of several Catholic grammar schools in the city, from grades Kindergarten through seven. Most Holy Rosary had small classes where the atmosphere was like family. The mothers prepared homemade hot lunches each day. Sloppy Joes were a favorite! There were many talent shows and Christmas pageants which were held in the big upstairs auditorium. In the basement was a small quaint church for prayer services.

To this day, so many years later, I am still in touch with a few of my grammar school classmates on social media. We are known as the "Holy Rosary Kids." We like to reminisce about our Most Holy Rosary days. They certainly were special.

In school I was just an average student and a very poor athlete. I was the notorious "Kid who was picked last" in gym class. While sports were never my forte, from early on I had a rich vocabulary and a love of reading. In fact, I can fondly recall a time when a fellow classmate told me that I used "too many big words" when I spoke!

Though I may have had an extensive vocabulary from a young age, I never really stood out and nothing in my schooling inspired me. That is, until I reached the fourth grade. This is where Mrs. Weber entered my life.

Jan Weber was my fourth-grade teacher. Mrs. Weber wasn't necessarily my favorite teacher, but she ultimately became an important part of my life. She was a tough teacher who took a special, though not in any way preferential, interest me and always encouraged me to read and write. Maybe Mrs. Weber had some sort of inkling of what I was to become.

I remember one class project where Mrs. Weber had us write a story in a book of blank pages she gave all of us, so that we could say we authored a book of our own. I always thought this was very special. Every teacher should do such a project with their students; allow them to freely create their very own book to be proud of and, say they had written, all by themselves.

Mrs. Weber was only at Most Holy Rosary for about a year. After she left, we wrote letters to each other and truly became friends. I would meet up with her from time to time and she always gave me small gifts, some of which I still have to this day. Amongst the many gifts she gave me throughout the years was a book with the poem Desiderata which I still cherish. My favorite quote from this poem has always been ,"You are a child of the Universe." That is how Mrs. Weber always viewed me; a child of the Universe.

I wish Mrs. Weber and Mrs. Farmer were here today to see what I've become, but I know they are always with me in spirit, cheering on my writing successes.

I've come a long way since Mary Street, fourth grade and my days at Most Holy Rosary School. I'm the author of two memoirs, several children's books, and a handful of published freelance articles. Like Mrs. Farmer, I became a writer from Perth Amboy. I thank both Mrs. Weber and Mrs. Farmer because, without them, I would not be who I am today.

Perth Amboy is only one small facet of the great Garden State, but it means so much to me. I encourage everyone reading this passage to one day take a ride, get off at exit 11 on the New Jersey Turnpike, head for Perth Amboy, and see for yourself the treasures it holds. Maybe you too will discover something about yourself along the way while overlooking the Raritan Bay.

Selected Poems
by Peter T. Donahue

Arboretum; Woodland

Between Brick City and Appalachia,
a landscape scraped by glaciers and left
more marbled with wealth and dearth than Victorian
endpaper. Grabens of gold. Horsts

of if-thens and dead ends.
It's hard not to picture the burrow of the field mice
as a *National Geographic* cutaway.
Look through the isometric corner

of the boiler room, through the two by fours
and cinderblocks to the rubble, humus,
leaf litter. You have to adjust your notion
of your house as a solid object. All

is permeable. There's always a route. You think
like them. You work like a Petrovich, find
the gap in logic, between two slats,
and fill it with epoxy foam.

Days later, we find the mice
by the boiler. Lying at the end of their flowcharts,
their if-thens, their close-parens.
A sweet stink of putrefaction.

In the Frelinghuysen Arboretum
they have all these plaques.
So-and-so donated this rare cultivar
of *coreopsis*, of flowering cherry.

But wander past the old mansion.
Past the gazebo, after the oaks,
the trail dips down into a gulley
of good old Jersey woodland.

Beech after beech, with elephant skin,
bears the knife-scars of heartbound
equations. The initials of those who love
Low-budget arboreal memorials.

I think I'll lie down in the leaves
and wait for dusk. Sixteen, I did
with my two best friends. Knifeless
we cut our initials into the night sky.

In Hedden Park, behind a rock
along the rapids of Wallace Brook.
Two teenagers smoking pot.
I nod to them. I am the weirdo,

checking under rocks for sacred
salamanders. Twelve hundred
of us to a square mile, we've learned
to zone "place of worship" inwardly.

Powerlines; Glacier

In Summerhill, the daughter of immigrants.
Her street a dried lava flow.
She walks her bicycle to the top.
Its frame and chain sing with August weight.

She pauses to look at Watnong hill.
Someone's shaved a stripe into it.
Trod by large-writ stickmen, like bikes
all frame and spoke, but without wheels.

Chakraless. They wait in line
for a chance to touch the source. For a waffle
sandwich on the boardwalk. For an agent
at the Motor Vehicle Commission.

Also, powder-blue, spheroid,
the town's crown chakra, an Om
to save mock-tudors from slack
tapwater, a tank emblazoned PARSIPPANY.

From the Lenape parsipanong.
The place where the river winds through the valley.
This time around, I am not the girl,
preparing to coast downhill forever.

I am not the bicycle, or even
the river of power winding over valley
and hill. I am the glacier, stretching
catlike as I nap on Watnong,

rousing to start my commute home,
dreaming of the ways the hills
I've carved here might regard each other
in eleven thousand years.

Smoke; Swarm

We wait in line for the Ferris wheel
at the carnival in Fireman's Field.
I watch a child leaping to flick
the hanging thread of smoke her mother's

cigarette lets out like a sounding line,
vibrating as it sounds every river,
which are all one and the same river.
We wait in line for cotton candy.

Phosphorescent as a seam
of Franklinite, we wait in line
for funnel cake at the Sussex County
Fair, jostled by the systole.

We wait in line for "U-Pick" pumpkins.
We're ferried on hay to a field new-mown,
a show-room of loose produce.
The sign meant "pick" as in "select."

We pile into the Honda Pilot
and highway to an orchard for Debbie's birthday.
We wait in line, prowling slow,
boustrophedon, through dust and dust.

We park at last. But aimless crowds.
A sign on the electric fence:
no apples left. Latecomer locusts,
we linger. People-watch from the tailgate.

For seven years I commute to Bridgewater.
Where 287 and 78
cross, one fall, a fever of cicadas.
I hear them but I never see one.

I imagine crawling out of the earth
after seventeen years to scream, fuck,
and die. The cicadas have their own
lines to wait in. Prime numbers.

Mountains; a Cellar

We become mountain peaks,
Tammany, Catfish, Rattlesnake, Sunrise,
High Point—waiting in line up
the Kittatinny Ridge to go sere.

We parked once in a spot marked V
by the condos up Watnong's eastern slope.
At nine or so, the fireworks of
half a dozen towns bloomed

all the way to the Watchungs, ridges
by day gone cyan in the isoprene haze
of the Great Eastern Forest, the unlikely
abundance of trees, exhaling trees.

From the top of the Tourne, at sunset, see
the pink facets of midtown Manhattan,
the calving front of another kind
of glacier. Gaze on it in grief.

A clicking July. Walking home
along Old Dover I push a plow
of air. Throw up a furrow of grasshoppers.
To my left, pavement. To my right, grass.

County owned. R-R
zoned. ("This shall not be construed to include
piggeries.") I am the bowsprit of a dry
ship cleaving hot air.

A brown bear lopes through the tax
map, Block 13, Lot
1.19. Fawns
look both ways before crossing the road.

I could only navigate
White Meadow Lake by guessing.
Criss-crossing streets named after tribes.
In my trunk a bass guitar.

The band rehearsed in a cellar lit
by Christmas lights, cramped as a carapace
and packed with noise. Nick's ride
the cracked Liberty Bell of punk.

A Noise

Slammed awake: a small earthquake
turns my stomach and pops a transformer
at the substation. Bang. On Twitter I ask
if anyone felt it. Meteorite?

Downed plane? Dirty bomb?
At three a.m. I always assume
New York is being nuked. Flashbacks
to masking tape on stripmall windows.

Mom told me, when I was a kid,
the trees along the barbed-wire fence
at Picatinny leaned out
because they sometimes dropped a bomb.

From the Lenape picatinana.
A mountain divided up in places.
This may not be California,
the Big One like an eschaton.

But New Jersey has faults of its own. The biggest
runs like a crooked smile between
the Newark Basin and the Highlands,
a caesarian scar through Nova Cæsarea,

Under the belly of Ramapo Mountain,
where a Native American tribe struggles
for breath, choked by the blood of its own
placenta. What was that noise? What?

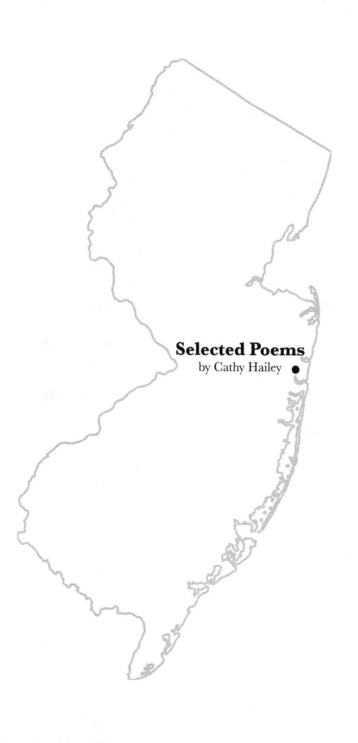

Selected Poems
by Cathy Hailey ●

Uncovering Heritage
Point Pleasant Beach, 1984

The lighthouse signal flashed like a bright star in a distant sky,
guiding us in our northward walk on the boardwalk.
Norma K II sailed out from the inlet on a night fishing voyage,
shining lights in a southeast path in search of bluefish.

The moon projected a cone-shaped beam that sparkled on rolling
ocean waves, crash deadened by a wide sandy beach, fog horns
echoing as we passed the last bungalow—windows stained glass,
fenced yard overgrown with weeds, cluttered with weathered antiques.

As we passed Jenkinson's Pavilion, the beach train's north station,
sea breeze stilled, displaced by wafting aromas of burgers grilling,
popcorn piling up behind glass, surf sounds drowned out by video
games beeping, skee balls pounding, pinball machines ringing.

Beyond the pavilion, at boardwalk's end, nature reawakened.
We settled on a bench to enjoy fresh sea breeze, inlet view,
jetty lined with monstrous gray rocks scattered with seaweed,
welcoming this rare moment with Yiayia to ourselves.

Here, with saltwater scents wafting up from Manasquan Inlet,
we asked Yiayia to share more of our family heritage. She told us
her life in Greece was actually a life in Kato Panagia, Tsesme,
Smyrni, Anatolia, Mikrasia, expelled to live as refugees on Chios,

nt to America with her sister by steamship in steerage, escape
om Kemal Atatürk's unacknowledged genocide. A secret:
er youngest brother taken by the Turks, hoping he was lucky enough
> be chosen for service in Turkey's army, a sacrifice to save his life.

ill—hope. I stumbled across a photograph—five men from Kato Panagia
 scout uniforms, wide brimmed hats, neck scarves, names in large Greek
ttering—Athanasios Kambanis. Something about his eyebrows, deep set eyes,
nall stature gives me hope he lived to be a man, rather than dying as a child.

Childhood Escape

I stand at the candy counter,
on the boardwalk at Jenkinson's Pavilion,
Point Pleasant Beach, New Jersey,
dressed in blue shorts
and a white cotton cropped top,
a small triangular print scarf around my head,
pulling my long curly dark hair
away from my face,

I request one red and one black hat,
then a slice of sugary bacon,
and ten pieces of licorice:
two each of brown, black,
red, green and purple.
The green is spearmint, not lime,
and brown is chocolate, my favorite
since I don't get it very often.

Most of the time I crave black,
but it's common at home.
The sales clerk smiles
and places each of my selections
in a small white paper bag,
only the colors of the licorice
peeking out from the top.
I reach into my pocket for my coins.

Two cents each times thirteen,
plus a penny for sales tax;

candy wasn't exempt
even in 1964.
The quarter comes out easily,
but I struggle with the pennies,
careful not to lose them
in the space between the boards.
I run to our Vetrini Row bungalow,
into the screened porch,
dump my precious loot
on our red checkered tablecloth,
pick out my favorites
before calling in the family
to share my sugary treasures.
I smile in sweet satisfaction.

Pinball Lord

He stoops over, feet planted
in the dulled hardwood floor
of Frank's Arcade, gripping
both sides of the machine
as if holding onto life,
stubby fingers nimble
as they flick buttons
to engage flippers—
sometimes synchronized,
often one at a time—
gatekeepers to oblivion,
his goal to keep a shiny
silver ball in motion,
rack up points,
face animated
as numbers rise,
bells clanging,
buzzers sounding,
his body more active,
pushing the machine back,
shaking it side to side
until he reaches crescendo—
a free game lighting
the world of Frank's Arcade—
and he relaxes, sweat dripping
from brows, body and arms still,
face beaming as he claims victory.
I watch mesmerized,
cheering him on, never
able to walk in his shoes

in a pinball challenge.
I still see my cousin playing
pinball in Point Pleasant Beach,
where we shared our best times,
Now he watches over me
as he plays pinball in the sky.

A Doll and a Dream

She's a doll in her square necked dress, high heeled pumps,
bright dark brown eyes, red lipstick smile across her face.
She enters the party New Year's Eve, last day of 1955,
and sees her dream speeding across the foyer to meet her.

It's all documented in eight millimeter film by cousins
who threw the party, hoping to match up Greek DC gents
with unmarried young ladies in Cedar Grove, New Jersey.
He introduced himself as he took her hand, led her away.

Music and dancing raged downstairs in this split level home,
and that's where they spent the evening dancing to Glenn Miller
and his orchestra—"In the Mood," "Moonlight Serenade,"
"That Old Black Magic," bewitching each other as they dance.

He leads her across the room, dipping her with a sweet kiss
to celebrate a promising new year, a brighter future—
frequent visits to her Montclair home, Packard drives
to Eagle Rock, dinner dates, carriage rides in Central Park.

Photographs document an engagement party crowded with cousins,
buffet of homemade Greek delicacies, honey-filled desserts, Greek
Orthodox wedding at New York's Holy Trinity Cathedral, reception
with orchestra and opera at the bronze canopied Fifth Avenue Hotel.

The magic continues on their honeymoon in subtropical Bermuda,
where they rock the Elbow Beach Hotel, winning a jitterbug contest,
then extending their stay at a New York journalist's guesthouse
where they eat grilled steaks and toast to a future life of happiness.

The doll and the dream fade when they bid farewell to New Jersey,
a more difficult life ahead beginning in a row house in a DC suburb,
where sharing a home with a mother-in-law challenges every day.
Still I take pleasure in seeing the spark of their magical Jersey start.

Oct. 29, 2012

Centipede
On
Stilt legs
The Seaside Pier
Ferris wheel love seats dangling
Mother Nature's war zone—the aftermath of Sandy.

Landmarks
by Tina Scott Lassiter

The road to would be the road back, something I couldn't have known at age five.

It was the summer of '63. Our family of six climbed into a burgundy Buick Electra 225, navigated the local streets of Washington, DC until we reached the highway that would take us north. I was none too thrilled. My maternal grandparents would no longer be 15 minutes away, our weekly sleepovers would no longer be. I was ever so excited! The unknown was ahead and whatever awaited would happen in the state of New Jersey.

Up to that moment, I'd only traveled to visit my paternal grand and great grandparents in Hampton, VA. The scenery on the southern route bore no resemblance to what my wide eyes catalogued as the car moved smoothly towards its northern destination. Looking back, there were industrial developments along this modern thruway, rest stops that a Black family like mine could pull into and make use of all the services provided. My face stayed glued to the window, particularly noting sights that captivated me. Much later in life I would understand that what I was doing was landmarking. Certain things came to serve as directionals or mileage posts wherever I went, the Delaware Memorial Bridge would be one of the first. As it loomed in the near distance, I couldn't wait to see it up close. That large of a structure over such a wide body of water...I gazed in awe! From that day on, it was a welcome reminder that within minutes, I'd be on the Jersey Turnpike. And the Garden State would be the state I lived in off and on for almost 30 years.

I have no idea how many times I've driven the Turnpike. I do know the exits that my family and I used frequently. When we moved from Washington, Exit 7 Fort Dix/McGuire Air Force Base was numero uno. A man in a tiny box took a paper ticket and some money from my Dad as we passed through onto a narrow two lane road. Cows, corn fields, and farms composed the landscape for miles. What I remember most is a store called the Shoe Barn, a red building with shiplap siding that was visible down the hill beside the Pike. Its presence gave me comfort or made me happy depending on the circumstance; it meant we would soon be back on Base or that we were going on some adventure. I also liked shopping in that rambling structure especially for shiny patent leather selections to adorn my feet. After two years, the family climbed into that trusty Buick to cross from the country lands of area code 609 into 201 suburbia. I bid farewell to the Shoe Barn as we headed farther north but always looked for it each time I was en route to Washington until that landmark no longer stood.

Exit 10 Metuchen, Perth Amboy fed into I-287. It led to a local road in North Plainfield that guided us to the sixth house from the corner on a cul-de-sac of seven dwellings. U.S. Route 22, a highway where any and everything could be found, felt like a second residence we were on it that often. It just terrified me! Lane changing automobiles careening along as if they were in a race unnerved me. I would close my eyes and pray that we'd hurry up and reach our destination. On either side and in the center of the road were stores big and small including, when we moved there, Two Guys, Great Eastern, Sears, and Shop Rite. Steer End, a drive-up that served burgers and fries, made me miss Big Boys, a DC drive-in, a little less. Best & Co. department store had a small location on the west side of the highway, signaling that the turn off for our abode was about a mile away. Whenever my grandparents visited from Washington, it was the best place to shop in their eyes, every pun intended. Many back to school outfits were purchased there until it and all the other stores mentioned closed their doors.

The view from the front porch of our two story house was Green Brook Park with its large playground, sandy softball fields, a babbling creek, foot bridges, and acres of land that seemed to stretch for miles. That first summer of running around, swinging on the swings, sneaking a wade in the water, and riding bikes flew by faster than I could peddle. I entered third grade that autumn wearing a Best ensemble. My sister and I were the first and only Black students to attend West End Grammar School that year. In Washington, my exposure to those who didn't look like me had been limited. I remember coming home asking, "Where are the brown people?" A week or so later the question was about the "N" word. We did manage to find friends amongst our school mates once they discovered that we were just kids as were they. The following year, other Black children enrolled at West End; my Dad told us more about our history and not a moment too soon. When the riots of '68 destroyed parts of Plainfield, the hurt behind the actions was something I was beginning to grasp. A path in my beloved park led up and over a bridge to the unrest heard night after night. Gunshots pierced flame lit skies solidifying within me a keen awareness of racial differences, a landmark of another sort.

On a winter break in 1971, during my freshman year in high school, we piled into a green Buick Riviera with my mother as my Dad, driving a navy blue Jaguar XJ6, led us about five miles east on Route 22. We crossed the highway and headed up into the hills of Mountainside. Our ranch style structure faced Watchung Reservation, an expansive terrain of forestry whose appearance delightfully changed with the seasons. I looked for deer in the morning while waiting for the yellow bus that stopped at the end of our driveway to take my sister and me down the mountain to Jonathan Dayton Regional High in Springfield.

My first week there almost broke me. Many of the students were less than cordial, aggressively competitive, and the college prep track was more advanced than the school I had transferred from. Resentment began to rev up within me; a mid-year move was not cool. It had taken me from the routine of familiarity that was my personal groove. No longer could I walk next door to visit friends, the only way to see them was when somebody drove me to their homes. Seemingly, new friends were not going to easily be found in the unfamiliar hallways and classrooms that I had to navigate. However, I became resolute in my desire to win folks over, take part in activities, excel in my studies. I graduated on the honor roll as a Who's Who American High School Student who had a diverse group of friends, who also had her license, and who was determined to conquer her fear of getting behind the wheel. I knew that driving and teaching myself how to navigate the many byways were companion tickets to exploring New Jersey on my own as well as getting to the people I wanted to spend time with. When my father and I headed west on 22 at the end of the summer, me and my former nemesis were well acquainted.

As we traveled along, Dad finally veered his Benz right and headed up then down the mountain sides to pick up Route 24 West (later known as I-78). This stretch of road was absolutely breathtaking. Gorgeous green hills were dotted with homes, beautifully constructed barns, and more horses than I'd ever seen roaming and grazing unattended. Mountains to somewhere beckoned from far in the distance. Much like when I took in my first glimpses of New Jersey as a five year old, I once again practically pressed my face against the window so I could absorb the majestic spaciousness of it all. I wondered why I'd never seen this part of the state, immediately made a pact with myself to further investigate the lush stretch between Mountainside and Bethlehem, PA. I would drive out to this area many times as I got older. The calmness of the countryside had spoken to my soul that first and only year I attended Lehigh University. I discovered that if I closed my eyes, I could imagine myself riding beside this picture of serenity anytime I wished as I sorted out life's issues, an ability I was familiar with when visualization techniques were introduced to me decades later.

Once my family moved to Mountainside, we drove through Westfield to pick up the Garden State Parkway. At Exit 129 we stopped at a toll, got a ticket and then proceeded south on the Turnpike to take me to Washington to finish my college education at Howard University. At the end of each school year, I plopped down in the back seat of whatever family car was driven to collect me. I couldn't wait to see what had changed on the interstates. More developments than trees, more lanes and more traffic than I remembered became the norm. The familiarity of direction and where it led remained constant despite the fact that many of my landmarks were gone. But there was a permanent new one. A wide U-shaped loop that led from the Turnpike to the toll booth at Exit 11 tickled me for some reason. I grew to love that swerve.

During the summers, eastbound 22 or 78 to the Parkway North marked the beginning of our vacation route to Martha's Vineyard. Prior to those trips taken in a Ford station wagon, I had only seen a small part of the most northern section of this thruway that spanned the length of the state. At the southern end were beach towns that I hung out in with my friends as an adolescent. As an adult, I would take the local train to the lovely town of Spring Lake or drive from DC to catch the ferry from Delaware to Cape May. I adored the swans found in the waters of the former and the dolphins swimming the Atlantic of the latter. Spring Lake shaped my desire to tuck away in a bed and breakfast near or on the water so I could read, stick my feet in the sand and fly my kite. Cape May cemented what became a life long commitment to finding places with claw footed tubs where I can soak in the quiet of morning, walk to the beach to collect shells and commune with the ocean, then sit down to write.

By 1986, a move one town over from Mountainside to Watchung into a place worthy of a spread in *Architectural Digest* had happened. College days had glided into working years combined with graduate school at New York University. I was driving the first car I would buy, a cream colored, four door Honda Accord. Interstate 78 was finally a straight shot from New York through Jersey to Pennsylvania since the construction that had been held up by environmentalists and local residents seeking an alternate passage or to stop the road altogether was completed. It was my preferred route to NYC in the evening after a long day at work and eventually in the morning when I became a full time student. Turnpike exits 14 or 16, depending on the traffic report, said hello and goodbye to me in the same day several times a week for months. That nervous teen whose face once reflected in my rear–view mirror no longer existed. In fact, I relished getting on the road. I once left Jersey at 6:00AM to do my Christmas shopping in Georgetown, DC and drove back from Washington that night. Never was I as glad to see the toll booth of the Turnpike as I wearily careened down the lanes of the Memorial Bridge. I knew that I was closer rather than farther from my bed, think I slept in it for a few days after that trip.

Prior to receiving my MBA, I was recruited to work for PepsiCo in Purchase, NY. The commute from New Jersey to my office was exhausting. I had to get up before dawn to hit the road early enough for me to beat the traffic back up at the Tappan Zee Bridge if I wanted to get to work on time. The evening rush hour and the thought of having to do it all over again the next day turned roads, tolls and exits into a blur. As mentioned, I had come to enjoy driving, considered myself an alert motorist until the morning I veered a little too far right on the Garden State Parkway about three exits before the Bridge. Another evening, I dozed off on Route 22 down the hill from my house. Shortly thereafter, I packed my bags and a U–Haul and hauled myself north until I crossed into New York. The decision to relocate probably saved me from becoming a NJ roadside statistic.

I returned to live in Watchung when I left my job and eventually moved to Manhattan to be closer to another. I no longer needed my second vehicle, a black Toyota MR2, so highways became bye-bye ways. If I wanted to visit family or go to DC, New Jersey Transit, PATH or Amtrak did the driving, allowing me to discover and appreciate an entirely different view of the state. Nine years and two apartments later on the Saturday after Thanksgiving, I borrowed a car, drove through the Lincoln Tunnel, said "farewell for now" to Exit 16, and got on the Turnpike, a moving truck packed with my possessions close behind me. From north to south, the landscape had changed as had I. There were less toll booth clerks; exact change and EZ Pass lanes had long since replaced connecting with an actual person. Convenience had robbed me of quick face-to-face hellos that added a pick me up to any trip. The expanded width of the Turnpike with lanes designated for "cars only" allowed me to avoid reckless truck drivers who reminded me of my initial experiences on Route 22. After Exit 4, a second lane had finally been added on both sides of the highway which seriously improved traffic flow.

The many roads that weave through and around the Garden State had "grew me up." What I had seen and learned at each stop and along each drive from whatever vehicle I operated or was a passenger in, had charted my route from girl to woman. Nothing would ever alter the thrill of seeing them crossing the Delaware Memorial Bridge. But on this trip, the first toll of the Turnpike would be the last thing I'd see in New Jersey before I drove across that vast structure. The road was taking me back to DC.

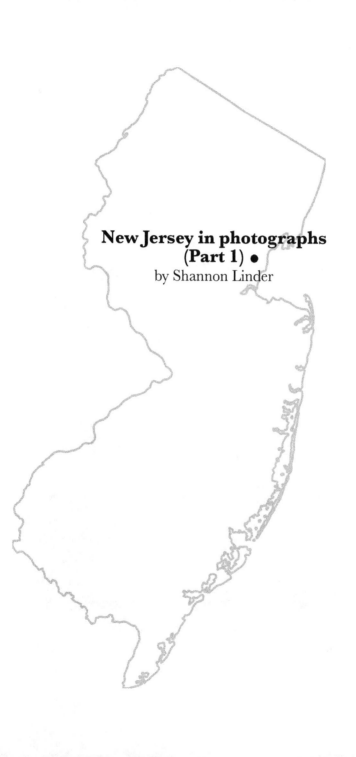

New Jersey in photographs
(Part 1) ●
by Shannon Linder

A self portrait in my Grandparent's home in Toms River. Behind me are portrait of my grandparents, aunts, uncles, cousins, my mom, my dad, and myself. The hou has since been sold and I cherish this photo as a memory.

*…ast of the Town, a run down liquor store with a fantastic, out-of-order neon sign.
…e first and only time I ever came here was when I was home for the summer between
…ege semesters, with an old boyfriend who drove a monster pick-up truck.*

Pilgrim Diner late at night. This diner has since been bulldozed and redone, but it was where all of the high school kids could go at 3AM for disco fries and breakfast platters since it was open 24/7. The staff were lovably eccentric.

*beloved mechanic's garage (Freegan's Automotive) featuring Anthony, who tire-
'y works on his motorcycle and keeps me company while I wait for an oil change.*

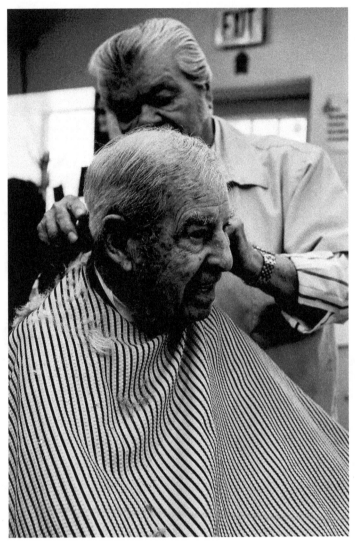

My grandfather getting a haircut on his 100th birthday.

My friend Max Kaplan (of Max Kaplan and the Magics) with his father, Eric Kaplan, jamming at their farm in Marksboro.

A man changing the signage at the Ringside Pub in Caldwell, which hosts one of my favorite open mics.

SynJersey
by Jill Ocone

Stay Salty

Jersey.

She's an addiction I simply cannot overcome.

I enter the world alongside the ocean and her salt water sweetness intoxicates me with my very first inhale. My brackish bloodline pulsates my distinct heartbeat in rhythm with the tides and the tempests.

I seize every opportunity to write beside the sea, where sand streams from my notebook as I tear it open to free my conscience and pour my life onto its crisp white pages.

Like the words forever in my soul, the boardwalk's splinters stuck in my soles endlessly burn and itch, but I can never fully remove either no matter how many times I perform surgery on my mind with a pencil and paper or on my feet with a pair of tweezers.

My pile of filled journals amasses taller than a stack of flapjacks as I scribble about my fuzzy recollections of hopping the Arts Center fence to see the Steve Miller show, slapping the newest Baja East Surf Shop sticker on the stop sign down the street, Jack Frost's glazing of the inlet rocks with ice, and the stinging humiliation from my failed poetry reading at The Inkwell's open-mic night, their signature dark-roast coffee the perfect metaphor for my disillusionment: bitter, black, and burning.

Rejection sucks, that's for sure, but I trudge onward

with that incomparable Jersey grit fueling my fire with tenacious resolve.

The diner, with its fascinating ambiance full of eclectic misfits who unknowingly become prototypes for my characters, lures me night after night, and it's there where I pen my best fiction long after most of the world is fast asleep. The drunks in the next booth spill their omelets all over their table, and the girl wearing smeared blue eyeshadow nearly spills into my booth as she rushes to the restroom. I mutter an expletive as the disco fries drip to stain my latest manuscript draft, as I now have to rename the drunk girl wearing smeared blue eyeshadow who nearly spills into the street because the cheesy brown gravy has blotted out her name.

Bruce and Jon encourage me to confess my own backstreets and the prayers I live on every day within my diary's leaves. I was born to run, dammit, and I want out. I declare to my page I've had enough of this jungle land that reeks of Jersey's bad medicine, but despite my hungry heart, I remove my brilliant disguise and acquiesce New Jersey is my home.

The ocean, a temptress, she renews her spell on me yet again through the ebb and flow of her hypnotic waves. Her seawater wine inebriates me and overpowers my eternal hangover of disenchantment, my scars soothed by her surf.

I never stop craving the roundabout that refuses to

slow down, and I can't get enough of the carousel that perpetually spins.

I ride on the coaster that rolls high and low, fast and slow, without ever disembarking the car, the adrenaline simultaneously sickening and exhilarating.

Word after word…

Ride after ride…

Day after day…

Wave after wave…

Page after page…

Year after year…

I am still here, with a pencil in hand and a keyboard at the ready.

Jersey.

My one-of-a-kind symbiosis.

Selected Poems

by Elizabeth Hays Gatti

Beyond the Breakers
for Eileen

Do you remember
That blistering-sand day
At Loveladies-by-the-Sea?
When you, Mary and I swam out
Far beyond the breakers, leaving Jon
Behind, abandoned on the shore?

We stripped and waved our bathing suits
Like multi-colored flags overhead,
Coded signals we thought he'd understand.
But he sank heavily to his knees in the sand,
Like an angry little boy, staring stubbornly
At the back of his unmoving hands.

Floating on the salty skin of the ocean,
We knotted our suits around our heads,
Pretending to be mermaids and whales,
Rising white-mounded on gelatinous waves,
Our laughter the tinkling of underwater bells,
The distant sound of ocean inside a shell.

But remember then, how the tide turned?
Our arms became too heavy, the beach too far
And the familiar grit of sand underfoot,
The joy of dry flesh, the homey smell
Of warm male necks seemed cruelly
Out of reach, waiting on another shore.

Life in the Garden State

We called out wildly, hoarsely, to Jon,
Willing him to come and rescue us,
But our voices only fluttered in place
Like seagulls battling a strong wind,
While he sat frozen, a staring sand castle
Waiting on the shore, watching us drown.

Blinded by the Light, Jersey Nights

My father was a convincing guy:
He told Ricky Blakemore and me
That bull frogs would jump
Right smack onto our handmade
Wooden rafts, if we went just before dark
And placed lighted candles on the boards,
Stayed down low in the tall grass
Waiting for the inevitable "plop"
Of the mesmerized frogs' chubby legs
Landing wetly on the dark wood.
We believed him without question.

Misty-hot New Jersey nights we'd creep away,
Down behind Mann's pond, near the riverbed,
Hunkered down, crouching in the reedy
Twilight, an Ever Ready flashlight at hand,
Bug-eyed, waiting for the blue blanket of night
And the throaty "chub-chub" of the frogs
Who miraculously resisted the allure of our trap,
Until finally we skulked off, frog-less
Into the Saddle River night.

Rick and I spent many a summer night
In search of frogs that never appeared.
We were waiting for love to emerge with the
Amphibians, but ended up hoodwinked
By the same guy who had fooled the Nazis
In a prison camp 20 years ago, staging phony
Break outs and bogus clandestine conspiracies
Just for momentary relief from the gnawing,

Relentless monotony of imprisonment,
To quash the humorless chatter of his guards.

Or how about the time Dad gave Alan Murray
A pepper apple he made by carving out
A tiny square, filling it with bitter black specks,
Then meticulously sealing the piece back in
With drops of candle wax melted with a match,
Just to see if the Murray kid would eat it.
He did, core and all, never blinking an eye.

And the Murray boy grew up, found love
That he couldn't possibly know would
Give him a disease then without a name;
Kill him with affection, one of the first of many.

And Rick went off to gig his own frogs
With a guitar and pen for his compass,
Evaded Vietnam somehow, making albums,
Coming home occasionally, but never
Again were we to stalk the wild night
Together beneath the starlit Jersey skies,
Before he died with his girlfriend
In a bloody multiple car crash,
And I plowed onward blindly alone.

Until finally Dad went, too, of lung disease
He'd ignored for heroically long, breathing
His last with us all around, helpless,
Amazed at his strength and presence.
We'd believed all his fantastic stories,
Knew him to be the All-American Boy,

Stay Salty

Born of the Depression, forged in war,
Despairing of suburban expectations,
Ultimately blinded by the light.

Trimming the black walnut

Standing sentinel over our property
For over three hundred years
Or so it seems from your majestic size:
At least thirty feet high and two wide,
Your dark presence taken for granted.

Your twin was hit by lightning
And taken down decades ago
According to my 91-year old mother
Who lies abed most days, recalling
The past, obsessed with these links.

And now you are dying, so it seems.
Huge branches and many are bare,
Looming ominously over the work area
Where the plant men work their trade,
Selling shrubs, annuals and garden geegaws.

Where once George Washington's troops
Limped up Paramus Road towards the
Haven of the Dutch Reformed Churchyard,
Now cars whiz by, occasionally stopping
To pick up a pumpkin, an ornament.

Everything has changed, and you've
Been the silent witness, since before
This broken United States was declared,
And now you're broken and maybe ready
To go back to the sacred Lenape soil,
While we limp on towards some unknown haven.

White Light Afternoon

Late afternoon at the shore:
Sun glints off yellow stones
Hard bubbles under bare feet
Feel of hot dry summer air
On cool skin, baking salt deeply
Into pores lazy with pleasure.

The sensuality of being:
Eleven years old in madras shorts
Walking to a friend's cottage
Passing Yucca plants in bloom
Hesitating to look up at the blue
Sky, knowing its purity will hurt,
Leave eyes stinging, blinded
By this distilled moment of childhood.

It was just like this:
Walking slowly over cracked cement
In Lavallette, New Jersey,
Bathed in the white light
Feeling one grain of sand at a time.

Fair Spirits

by Margaret Montet

I had visited the New Jersey State Fair once, with my sister when I was ten, and we left her two babies with our parents so we could escape there. At the fair, potential riders waited in line for the Ferris wheel, merry-go-round, Tilt-A-Whirl, and others, but my sister and I, used to the more substantial and elaborate rides at Great Adventure and the Wildwood Boardwalk, opted out of riding rides. We strolled by the wheels of chance and games of skill, and probably ate some not-nutritious fair food. I remember lots of bright lights creating a carnival atmosphere, and lots of people having a joyful time.

Besides that actual trip to the fair, there are but two memories still in my head from when the NJ State Fair was held in my town: fifth grade boys talking about speedway races in the back of our classroom, and my high school friend Patty telling me her mother won ribbons there for her sewing. I remember an exquisite navy-blue blazer she made for Patty which made my jaw drop.

Life-sized and giant Impressionist people populate the park now, straight out of early twentieth-century French Impressionist paintings. This is Grounds for Sculpture, a popular and unique place to walk and look at art. Twenty-first-century visitors mingle with the Impressionist characters, conjured from cast bronze mostly, and I see the humans' photos on social media. I do it, too, but I try to be more creative. On one visit I brought a small stuffed polar bear named Knut who wears a blue sweater and posed him with the art for photos. I meant to be silly, but it turned out Knut was really good at showing scale. In one photo he sits on a giant sculptured lady's black shoe as if he's an ornament. Without Knut, anyone looking at my photo would not know how huge that lady is. In another photo, he's on a French couple's alfresco table next to the wine. He sits atop a painter's satchel in another.

At Grounds for Sculpture, the visitor finds two kinds of art: realistic and representational like the characters rendered from recognizable Impressionist paintings, and abstract objects. Sculptors sculpt sculptures with museums or outdoor installations in mind, but this huge sculpture garden must be a dream for them. How do sculptors come up with ideas for those abstract sculptures? Do they start with a texture they'd like to represent, or do they have a lump of clay, stone, wood, or some material that inspires them into a work of art? What was the inspiration for the giant sinking into the New Jersey soil, I wonder, or the sea creature that looks like a giant snail, or the hideous larger-than-life creatures cooking parts of a guy named Larry in a giant cauldron, or Gloria Vanderbilt's mixed media Heart's Desire? I know a few sculptors—I should ask.

Please understand that Grounds for Sculpture is not a boring, flat grassy property adorned with sculptures. There are landscapes, stands of bamboo separating areas, roaming peacocks, and water features. Monet's green bridge from Giverny, portrayed in many of his Impressionist paintings, is there, over by the restaurant. On one recent visit, I met a young woman on that bridge who was gob–smacked by this wonderland: "I can't believe how cool this place is! I live about an hour away, but I'm going to be here all the time!" I wonder how much she knew about its state fair history.

I discovered on a recent walkabout that there is a fine curated collection of trees at GFS, clearly labeled. This thrilled me because I am trying to learn trees, by their bark, leaves, fruits, shape, whatever. I often say that I'd be a much better birder if birds would wear signs or nametags so that I'd know what kind of bird they are. They refuse to comply, so I am forced to take their picture and compare it later to the illustrations in my bird identification books. I can skip this step at Ground for Sculpture because of the tree signage. My tree ID book becomes merely a supplemental resource.

Sounds of racecars on the speedway seem to echo through the park now, until I realize those are not racecars but SUVs, trucks, and sedans on the nearby highway. I prefer to think of those sounds as spirits of the old racecars which were finished racing here by 1980. Sometimes I look at empty lots where houses once stood. I find myself imagining that space, the air above the ground, as someone's universe. A person, or a family, once slept, ate, read, watched TV, argued, and otherwise interacted in that space once which is now just air over an empty lot. Does that space carry the memory, the essence, of those people? This is how I think of Grounds for Sculpture except that J. Seward Johnson, the artist who created those cast-bronze Impressionist figures and others, placed his atelier here and then imagined his sculpture wonderland where the fairgrounds once stood. This is not empty space, but space endowed with new spirit. Does it still carry the essence of fair-goers?

There are a few clues to the Grounds' fairground history for today's visitors. The Domestic Arts Building is there, and the Motor Exhibit Building, still named as such, but both of them re-purposed. Between them used to be a third building, but this one was moved across the path and sits alone. Repurposed as the Museum Building, it features exhibits when there is not a pandemic raging. All of the buildings have been closed when I walk there in 2020 and 2021, except for a few very essential services for the public. Offices are open, and I imagine the atelier is, although Mr. Johnson died recently. Other artists work there, too. The location of the speedway grandstand is visible and has been incorporated into an installation of extra-large busts of nine men and one woman. I love to practice aperture-priority photography here, in other words, focus on one head and have some others blurred in the background. Each of these giant busts has a personality all its own.

In an attempt to keep active and entertained during the pandemic, I purchased a membership to the Grounds for Sculpture, simply to have an thought-provoking place to walk. I imagine the fairgrounds being there for decades, and people visiting with their prized livestock and peach preserves. Those boys from fifth grade would show up at the speedway with their dads, probably. They've moved on now, but are their spirits and memories alive still at this place? I don't know. You probably don't know, either, but I imagine someday we'll find out how spirits, ghosts, and souls work. My late sister's and my snobbery about the rides would be part of the collective memory of the state fair, I suppose, but so would Patty's late mother's blue ribbons and those fifth-grade boys' racecar fantasies.

Selected Poems

by Elizabeth Edelglass

Lake Hopatcong

Plastic horsie tube hugs my body,
too-short arms hug horsie head,
tight. Plastic and Coppertone
and seaweedy smell of lake.
Does seaweed grow in fresh water?
Memory doesn't care.

Fresh: untainted, invigorating, fit for drinking.
Green mud slimes my toes
in mirky depths I cannot see,
balancing on ballerina tips
to skirt sharp rocks,
mud squelching, sucking.
And waves. Does a lake have waves?
Memory, again. Maybe just the riot
of people jumping, splashing,
thrashing, shouting, too crowded
for swimming, if I knew
how to swim.

Sister, in her black tire tube,
rank of rubber,
floats close—
trusted memory—sister
grasping tight
my horsie head.
I am four, sister is seven.

Mother and father on blanketed shore
under green-and-white striped umbrella
with rusty struts where mother
will hang my wet suit, after I change
into dry, right there, in the scrum
of blankets and beach chairs,
so many people, so many eyes
trusted not to look.
Then mother will unpack sandy
tuna sandwiches. Was there sand?
I remember grit under nacre nails
and, always, mother's tuna sandwiches.

But that comes later. What
are they doing now, mother
and father alone on the blanket,
alone in the scrum
of blankets and beach chairs,
alone without sister and me?
Mother with her long legs
and the conical cups of her corseted
swimsuit. Father with his lips
that gave life to my horsie tube
and his trusted arms
that carried me and sister's tire tube
over scalding sand—yes, sand—
to wave us off at water's edge.

Mother and father on the blanket,
while I am alone in the water,
alone without a grownup—
surrounded by grownups,

but no grownup of my own.
Only sister.
I am four, sister is seven.
Alone together,
drifting in my horsie tube,
through crush of oily bodies,
splashing, pushing, roiling waters—
out and out
towards the barrier rope.

Hopatcong, from the Lenape
word for stone water,
or stone over water.
Stone: mineral, meteorite, gem
that can skip across water
one, two, three, four times.
Out and out
towards the barrier rope,
suckling mud abandons
my searching toes,
horsie hugs my slithery waist,
mother and father imagined
on the blanket, sister
in her tire tube, rank of rubber, reaching,
reaching for horsie head.
Sister who—I trust—knows
how to swim.

Exposure

Two sisters, two months pregnant, twice in this life.
Two rounding bellies not yet beating, awaiting life.

First white cotton bra, first brown leather purse, first Tampax
before I ever looked for blood, gifts from you who knew my life.

Scratchy sand and striped umbrellas, Sundays at the Jersey shore, starfish
caught to dry on rocks, and jellyfish, casually abandoned, melting life.

Two sisters in baby-doll pjs, unseen on upstairs landing, smoke wafting,
cocktails clinking, sometimes shouting, bare arms prickling, discovering
life.

Two identical jersey tops bought on different coasts to flaunt our swelling;
you moved east, we met at mother's, dressed as one—coincidence, or life?

First red VW convertible beetle, your arm out the driver's side, mine
out the passenger's, yours freckled, mine suntanned, unscarred by life.

Two sisters side-by-side, plastic shovels dig to China, sand crabs, sunburn,
sea glass, once a bullet from father's war—did he ever take a life?

Ferryboat visits, back and forth across east coast waters, waves
boiling rounded bellies, drumming foot-beats seeking life.

Two sisters in dark basement, projector flickering family movies,
mother carrying cakes or turkeys, always smiling, unlike life.

First boyfriend, first kiss, first love, first unwanted kiss, first

Stay Salty

miscarriage, first cancer—phone wire the curly umbilical cord of life.

Shifting sands on Jersey shore, bricks and concrete, walls and cistern storm-exposed, century-buried structure meant for saving life.

Two babies, twice—first boys, then boy/girl—red hair, brown hair, freckles or not, unidentical cousins sharing life.

16mm home movies, red painted fingers cutting our cakes, birthday-after birthday, until. Projector extinct. Who will know the stories of our life?

Road Map

st photo, a boy (you), a girl(me), hand-in-hand, new love.
 pony tail, your sixties 'stache, college hillside of New England.

ury Park, Deal Beach, boardwalk, salt water taffy always craved but
er loved, sleepy ride home from the silken shores of my New Jersey.

at did we know of love? Tentative touch, sharing stories—who are you?
o am I? who will we become? we/us, something unknown, a couple, new.

tty sand of Long Island Sound, rambling summer cottage, outdoor shower,
fish sailboat, bare feet leathered, summer visits to your New Haven.

d-dune breasts, valley waists, dips and rises discovered between thighs,
es and undertow, pulling, pulling, unrelenting, our bodies shockingly new.

k the boxes, pack the car, moving, moving for your doctor dream, buy me a map
ew streets, find the butcher, the baker, the down-the-block best new friend.

s to work past the White House, wash your white coats reeking of anatomy
maldehyde, take my temperature every morning until… birth, a boy, our
baby.

nily circle, uncles arguing, aunts cooking, a plumber, a painter, a wallpaper
ger, memories of Philip Roth, the Weequahic Jews of my mother's
wark.

low you to Motor City, empty bed while you practice on people,
hoscope and swing set, preschool and pregnant belly, our new family.

Stay Salty

Family circle, uncles and aunts under stones, where the Jews are buried down the Jersey Turnpike, Bethel to Central to Dinah, tracing the roads to each new grave.

Paying bills, children squabbling, your mother and father for Sunday dinners, one more baby, gritty beach, forty years lived in your New Haven.

Children grow, flee, follow their own roads. Dunes droop, valleys swell, Bethel to Central to Dinah, follow me someday, forever, to the new-turned soil of New Jersey.

Jump In

by Patrick Lomnardo

I never embraced my passions as a kid. I was too afraid of the stigmas attached to the interests I held. Reading appeased me, while my friends were terrified of it. Writing excited me, while my classmates detested it. There was always this dichotomy: something was either good or bad, fun or boring. There never was a gray area. I usually leaned toward the less popular side but was quick to change my mind when confronted about it. As a result, I never was fanatical about anything. A complete stranger could tell me it was snowing outside when it clearly was eighty-five degrees and sunny, but still I would agree with him. What did I know anyway? I was no meteorologist. I just thought I wasn't opening myself up to ridicule, when instead I only was closing myself off to the rest of the world. I was ignorant to the vast oceans of diversity and acceptance that quietly govern countless pockets of this planet, including right here in New Jersey.

When I was in college, I worked part time as a server at a local chain restaurant. I made a handful of friends I still talk to now, ten years later, including my wife, who didn't find me the least bit funny or interesting the first time we met. That likely hasn't changed, especially after marriage. But one friend found me hilarious, and we worked together almost every shift. After a year of working together, he found it appropriate to tell me he has been in a rock band for the past decade. "We're called Tumbleweed," he said, standing next to me in the back corner of the restaurant, staring out at an empty dining room. "You should check us out. We're playing a show next

Thursday night."

I had friends in high school who wrote music and performed as often as a teenager's schedule and strict curfew would allow, but I never actually went to see them play. I always told myself I ought to go to one of their shows, but I habitually made excuses so I could stay home. I frequently played sports and hung out with my friends, but that didn't mean I'd choose going out over locking myself in my room and reading if I had the option. I enjoyed doing nothing. I was never lazy, but it wasn't difficult for me to get into the spirit of loafing. As I got older, my parents recognized that sending me to my room when I'd misbehave was less of a punishment for me and more of a reward. I didn't need modern technology to keep me busy; I had books and a pair of glasses. What else was there? On particularly restful nights, the only way one could get me out of the house was to bribe me with trips to Borders, the now-defunct book, music, and movie store. As much as I loved music, going to a live show was unheard of. I would have scoffed at the notion. "A concert? With all that noise? But how will I be able to concentrate on my book?"

One of the first shows of which I sat through the entirety was in the basement of a church in my hometown. Maybe it was the divine presence that guided me out my front door that evening, or maybe it was my friends begging me not to skip another show. Whatever it was, it overpowered my desire to dig into another David Sedaris book, and I found myself at church on a Saturday night, praying for "just one more song." I loved the music. I loved the noise. When the show was over, I wasn't ready to hole myself back up in my room just yet.

That show introduced me to several impressive acts, and I made a point to attend a number of future humble performances over the years, whether I was acquaintances with the musicians or not. New Jersey hotspots for this genre are New Brunswick, Asbury Park, and Hoboken, but that doesn't stop the entirety of the state from rocking out every Friday and Saturday night. There are shows all year round, and with Philly and New York just a highway away, you will never have trouble finding some indie shows for the weekend.

There's a fervent energy within the independent music scene that is lost at your typical sold-out arenas. In these intimate settings, twenty-five people can conjure as much fire and fury as the twenty-five thousand who surf the web on their mobile phones during a Skrillex concert. Indie shows are often in-your-face intense, and everyone in the audience shows their engagement, either by dancing, head-banging, or accidentally knocking someone or something over. No matter how small or how crowded the venue, audiences disregard their environment and throw their arms in the air with more ferocity than my grandmother when she ties someone during bingo. I'm usually the guy hiding behind a used Nikon, though—the one who creeps to the middle of a small group, snaps a photo of the performing band, and scurries away, not to be seen until the next band takes the stage. But I always enjoy an indie show, regardless of my phantom tendencies. At most, a local concert is an opportunity to connect emotionally with true, unencumbered artists whose boundless nature allows them to thoughtfully and thoroughly share what's secluded in the deepest fissures of their tumultuous minds. At least, it gets me out of the house.

A lot of the time, learning about the musicians and their backgrounds and inspirations is just as enjoyable as their distinctive tunes, and I never miss an opportunity to get to know more about these artists and what they are into. Their interests, ambitions, histories, and desires extend way beyond the flawed connotation of the pot-addicted punks and hipsters who grace made-for-TV movies. They're different, complex people. Every single one of them.

The indie music scene in New Jersey is one of the most diverse you will find. It features some of the most talented and knowledgeable artists you've never heard of and, frankly, probably never will. That does not diminish their quality or determination, but judging by the immensely tough competition in this field, as well as America's insatiable appetite for stellar piles of musical feces, this talent may appear wasted. However, the skills of these musicians are not wasted; they're very much utilized to produce soulful, authentic tunes you will never *feel* anywhere else.

New Jersey bands regularly travel out of the tri-state area to perform for small audiences who dig the east coast flavor, but you'll also find a plethora of bands from the other forty-nine states coming to our neck of the parkway. You may lie in bed and listen to music by artists from other states, but until you stand five feet from a Midwestern boy screaming his heartache into a broken microphone, you don't know squat about your fellow countrymen. The experience is different, because it *comes* from somewhere different and it's presented to you in a respectable setting, as opposed to a sort of artificial environment created from expensive recording equipment. These out-of-area artists present new ideas and philosophies, which are facilitated by an almost foreign dialect. Their vernacular is familiar yet unrecognizable at times. In other words, they're usually *friendly*. If you are introduced to these friendly artists, you'll spend a decent portion of your time carefully picking out your words so that you don't inadvertently offend your new friend with traditional New Jersey jargon that's considered rude in normal societies. You shouldn't call anybody a "shoobie" or mock a tourist who isn't familiar with jughandles if you want to befriend them, for example. If you want to be hospitable, offer a visitor pork roll or recite the legend of the Jersey Devil.

On one occasion, I made a friend from Nebraska who had recently swam in the Atlantic Ocean down in Cape May, despite February's frigid weather. "It's different for you guys," he told me, "because you're always right by the ocean, so it probably seems like no big deal. But in Nebraska, we're right in the middle of the country and rarely come out this way. So when we're by the water, we don't miss an opportunity to jump in."

We got to talking about his band and their past tours and what he does to fund these mini laps around Uncle Sam's melting pot. Then he asked me a simple question in an effort to get to know *me* better: "What are you into?"

What am I into? I repeated in my head. I wasn't sure how to answer that. It was easy enough to figure out. Books and dessert—that's what I'm into. I also enjoy writing, yelling at malfunctioning technology, and doing absolutely nothing whether or not it's convenient. I've watched *The Office* at least twenty times through and own all seven seasons of *Boy Meets World* on DVD. I've had turtles for two decades. I stack boxes of books and comics by my bedroom window. I keep a yardstick next to my bed so that I can shake my ceiling fan when it starts to make that insufferable rattling sound. (It usually helps to make the rattling go away, believe me.) But what am I *into*? I continued to list my likes and habits in my head, but I knew this wasn't what he was asking about.

I began to think perhaps he meant to ask what I do for a living as well as in my free time. But he asked the question way too politely, and it caught me off guard. Us northeasterners ask, "What do you do?" as if it's an accusation rather than genuine interest in someone's employment or hobbies. We'd ask it in the same manner a boss would ask a subordinate if he was stealing, or in the same way a mother would reprimand her child for misbehaving at school. "Are you happy with yourself?" the mother would ask her middle school son who had just pulled the fire alarm, and he'd bow his head in a shameful silence, just as I might if a New Jerseyan asked me, "What do you do?" But Midwesterners found a way to ask that same question politely, and pleasantly coarse New

Jerseyans have no way to answer without returning a discourteous response out of force of habit.

So, as I continued to ponder his question, I chuckled and looked toward the exit. I scratched the back of my head. Maybe I spent too much time in books than in public, and it was showing. *What the hell do I do? What am I into?* I asked myself again. "I write," I thought about answering, but that wasn't what he was looking for, was it? So, instead, I said, "Ah, you know…" and my voice trailed off, and we stood in silence for a few more moments while he awaited my response.

After nearly thirty seconds passed, he bobbed his head the way I supposed all Midwesterners do when they are no longer interested in you but want to remain polite. Then he said, "Cool, man," and stepped away to greet another concertgoer.

I've never been asked that question by a New Jersey musician, but considering that my days of enjoying indie shows are not over, I've learned to prepare myself for future questions asked by naturally polite out-of-staters.

"What are you into?" I may be asked again one day.

Now, I'll just jump right into it. "I'm into supporting local music," I'll say, and I will return a friendly grin and tell him all about the diversity of New Jersey's independent music scene as he respectfully smiles and nods his head and learns about what I'm into, regretting that he ever asked.

Stay ●
by GR Lear

Stay

by GR Lear

Stay Salty

Stay off the tracks

Stay right

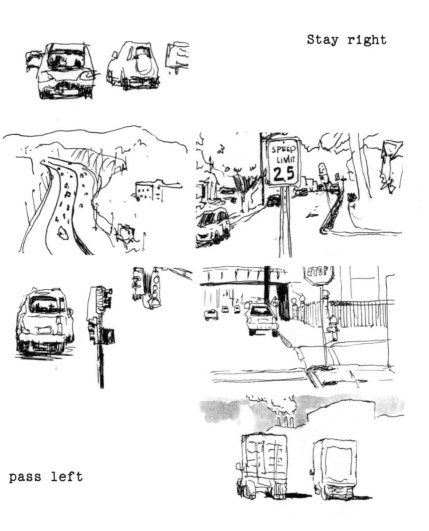

pass left

Stay Salty

Stay in

Stay warm

Stay

on the farm

Stay Salty

Stay

still

Stay

gold

Stay Salty

Stay

salty

A Song for the Water

by A.J. Pellegrino ●

When Mr. Morrissey moved into the house directly behind mine, I was fifteen years old. The previous owners of the house, Mr. and Mrs. Hilder, had been prominent members of the community and had lived there far longer than I had been alive. Cancer had taken Mr. Hilder in his early sixties and Mrs. Hilder was never quite the same after that. This was the only Mrs. Hilder that I had ever known. A Mrs. Hilder that rarely left her house and took no better care of her yard than she did herself.

When my family moved in Mrs. Hilder was seventy-three; her swimming pool was a light green and her yard had begun to take on a life of its own. By the time I was nine, the plants across the property were long overgrown; coiled around cement, bricks, and any fence it came into contact with. It created a shield of nature to protect Mrs. Hilder from the world and gossip she had retreated from.

It was my birthday when my mother learned that Mrs. Hilder had passed away. Her son, Scott, left notes in everyone's mailboxes and then began trying desperately to make the house presentable to sell. Everyone in the neighborhood went to the open house, having talked amongst themselves for years about the state it must have been in by the end.

The house itself was in fine shape, but there was nothing to be done about the backyard.

You could hear Scott hack away back there for a few months, but he must have prayed that a lover of foliage would find it a project. I don't truly believe Mr. Morrissey was a lover of foliage.

I do believe he liked the privacy it offered him.

Mr. Morrissey should have been a grumpy man in his mid-sixties. He should have grumbled around his property, taking care of the pool in the short-lived summer heat. This was the image I had of Mr. Morrissey as I heard him move into his new house, and I kept this image of him for a few weeks after as I heard him cursing about the state of the pool.

Mr. Morrissey, however, was a man who could have been no older than forty. He had a large pick-up truck and, as far as anyone could tell, he was very single; which was odd for our neighborhood. His hair was thick and dark with small flecks of gray highlighting its layers. He must have been powerfully built under that t-shirt and faded jeans because he had been hauling in bag after bag of salt and pool equipment on that dull summer morning.

"Hey!" He yelled and snapped me out of my daze. "What are you doing back here? You can't be on my property."

"S-sorry," I stammered and shot up from the ivy I had been hiding in; a heat crept from my neck to my cheeks. Mr. Morrissey hadn't moved from his spot by the pool but had dropped the bag of salt onto another at his feet. His face was red from exertion and his chest rose and fell in a harsh pant. I couldn't tell if he was angry or winded. "I was - I was just - "

"Does your friend think I can't see her?"

"The friend" he was referring to was Melinda Lourde. She had been my best friend since grade school and she was laid out flat at my feet trying to make herself as small as possible, gripping my ankle and the ivy with wide eyes. It had been Melinda's idea to sneak through the loose fence panels of my yard and try to get a good look at the new neighbor.

"I've heard some of my mom's friends talking," Melinda giddily explained, jumping onto my bed. "They all say that Mr. Morrissey is a dreamboat."

"Oh yeah?" I asked, glancing at her in the mirror as I attempted to brush the bumps from my hair. "Dreamboat?"

"Well, no," Melinda said and tried to get a look out the window to my left. It overlooked what could be seen of Mr. Morrissey's yard which was just a blanket of heart shaped leaves of varying shades of green. "But they said he's just as attractive as Mr. Mitchells."

"No way," I said and snapped the rubber band from my wrist around my handful of hair.

Mr. Mitchells was the history teacher that had just about every girl at our high school swooning; and it would seem, some of the mothers as well.

"Way. Dora's mom confirmed it. She saw him working in his yard last weekend, and she said, and I quote 'I'd let him tend my flower any day'."

Ten minutes later, we found ourselves squatting with our backs against my fence and a thicket of leaves and bushes in front of us. We could hear Mr. Morrissey moving back and forth throughout his yard but had no clear view of him through the vines.

"We're going to have to crawl through when he goes back out to his truck," Melinda whispered and peeked through some vines.

"He's definitely going to see us."

"No way, this shithole yard is so overgrown he

wouldn't be able to see anything if it snuck in."

"Okay," I said slowly. "What about spiders? Mom says this place is probably crawling with them."

"Don't say crawling," Melinda shuddered and rubbed her arm lightly against mine. I shuddered as well as the sounds of boots echoing away from our hiding spot could be heard.

"Now's our chance, go!"

I had been grounded for the rest of the week. That hadn't stopped my mom from questioning me about what Melinda and I had seen in the backyard and then relaying that to anyone she could think of. This left me with a lot of time to stare out of my bedroom window down at the blanket of leaves that muffled the grunts and curses of Mr. Morrissey. It also ensured that I heard a loud splash and an unearthly chirping sound a few days after our failed reconnaissance.

I began to sit in my backyard by the hole in our fence with my Walkman in my lap and my headphones resting on my ears. My mom never suspected that I wasn't blasting the CD that Melinda had made me for my birthday. No one looked that close, so I didn't need to answer any weird questions about why I was listening to Mr. Morrissey stomp around his backyard. Mostly, I just heard him muttering soft soothing words to something batting gently at the surface of the, now functioning, pool.

It was three days before I heard that same chirping sound. The noises had started flowing gently, almost musically, along the warm wind that blew the canopy of leaves out of place. By this time, my mother had started asking, 'why are you sitting outside by yourself?', and 'why don't you want to go play with your friends?'.

I called Melinda to satisfy my mother, even though I knew that she was visiting her cousins until the end of the month. She had complained about it and I had sympathized with her for weeks. I almost felt bad using it as my cover, but it was enough to show my mother that I had put in an effort. She really thought I should try playing with the boy Shawn down the block.

I went back to listening and waiting and becoming ever more curious when I heard the noise again. They sounded like soft clicks and long, slow throaty pulses, almost like someone was trying to imitate a bird but wasn't really sure what they sounded like. The noises were always met with Mr. Morrissey's hushed gravely murmurs. This time, when Mr. Morrissey's hushed tones stopped, I heard his boots stomp away in the direction of his driveway and then the slamming of his truck door and the engine turn over.

I sprang up from my sitting position for the first time in days. This was it, this was my chance to find out what was in that pool. I might not get another one.

I pulled off my headphones and dropped to my knees near the hole in my fence and eyed it wearily. It hadn't sounded like Mr. Morrissey pulled up any of the ivy since our little excursion into his yard. Which made sense, I thought as I dragged myself back to my feet. If I were hiding something back there, I would make sure I never pulled that stuff up.

I paced quickly as my mind worked to keep up. I had no way of knowing how long he would be gone so I had to work fast. My eyes landed on one of the many dense foam softballs littering my backyard and I lobbed it as hard as I could over the fence and through the canopy. I winced as I heard a loud, wet *thunk* which could only mean it had landed in the pool.

I sprinted into the house, passed my mother with a hurried explanation and was out the front door. By the time I reached Mr. Morrissey's house, I was clutching at a stitch in my side. I moved as quickly as my burning lungs would allow towards the fence door that led to the backyard. I tried to stop my hands from shaking, but I had too much anxiety swirling around in my stomach to keep them steady as I unlocked the door and pushed it open.

The backyard looked more put together than it had from the ivy by the fence. The pool was no longer half empty or a gross greenish color. It was filled to the tiled border with water so thick with salt that it swirled and acted as a shield to obscure whatever lurked below its surface.

The quiet hum of the pool equipment echoed off the vegetation to provide an eerie song. The smell that hit me as I moved closer to the middle of the backyard was no longer that of cooked spinach. It reminded me of the ocean.

The neon softball that I was looking for was sitting patiently in the grooves of the patio titles that surrounded the pool. Which was strange, because the ball sounded like it had landed in the pool. Yet there it was, with a wet trail leading from the edge to its current resting place.

I inhaled, long and quiet, as I eyed the slowly rippling pool water, now somewhat regretting my rash decision. I slipped out of my flip flops, tiptoed my way towards the ball, and as I knelt down to inspect it I heard the light patter of fingertips drumming against the patio tiles right behind me. I froze.

I remember closing my eyes tightly, as tightly as I would in the dark when I used to wake up in the middle of the night and willed all of the monsters in my room to disappear. So tightly that I could see colored orbs appear in the dark, and all the while the light patter never let up. I took a breath to try and stop my racing heart, but it was no use. I turned my head towards the pool and opened my eyes.

Once the colored orbs had disappeared from my vision, I saw that there were indeed fingertips drumming against the pavement. Long, thin fingers with a dark purple at their nail bed and a shimmering lilac encasing each knuckle. As my vision came into better focus, I realized that shining lilac was small clusters of scales that moved fluidly with every movement those fingers made. My eyes followed the fingers over the pool edge to where the top of a head was peeking out of the water; just enough to reveal the eyes, forehead, and hair of what looked to be a girl, maybe a few years older than me.

She wasn't entirely human. The same dark purple that was surrounding her nail beds was also surrounding her hairline, and bleeding upwards so that it looked as though her hair was the same color. Her eyes were what made me turn my whole body towards the pool and crawl slowly towards its edge. They were golden and lively, almost like her irises were pools of their own.

As this not quite human lifted her face further from the water to meet mine, I saw that she had lilac scales that started at the curve of her cheekbones to meet the ones resting under her eyebrows. I stopped crawling and rose to my feet, gathering a hold over my curiosity and intending to turn away. The creature rose as well.

Her body glistened as water droplets formed, then slid off of her scales and dripped down her stomach. The start of her breasts had scales that shimmered in the sun bordering them and traveling down her stomach at the crease of her abs. These same scales traveled up her chest to meet her jawline and connect with the scales that surrounded her eyes. Her hands rested where her fingers had been previously drumming and I could see that these same scales began at her elbows and traveled up the backs of her arms to circle her shoulder blades.

I felt a heat begin at my chest and spread up my neck as I stared openly at her breasts then down to where her hard stomach met a fin that was made up of the same lilac scales that adorned her body and shimmered to that deeper purple as they hit the sun. Her tail beat rhythmically against the surface of the water as she raised one of her arms and pointed at the softball in my hand.

I looked at it dumbly, still trying to keep my eyes from wandering back to her breasts and the heat from spreading further up my face. I gripped the softball tightly and then thrust it out in front of me without meeting her gaze.

"I'm sorry I threw this at you. I didn't mean to - would you like it?" I asked with my eyes glued to the ground.

After a few seconds, I chanced a quick look at her face. Her eyebrow was raised at me and her head was tilted ever so slightly to one side.

"I'm sorry," I tried again, staring into her beautiful eyes. "Did it hit you? You know - " I pantomimed the ball hitting me in the head and she smiled. She shook her head and made a "come here" motion with her finger.

"No," I said, even as I felt myself taking a step towards her. "No, I really should go."

I suddenly started to feel like the rest of the world wasn't real and that right here, in this pool, was everything I ever needed.

She opened her mouth and that same throaty pulsing came out. Up close it sounded like an impersonation of a robin, then she made a loud click in the back of her throat. I saw the slits near the base of her throat flutter as she did this. I went to say something else, stopped myself, and turned away towards the driveway.

A sloshing noise sounded behind me and that same chirping noise floated gently towards me. I turned back to her and saw that she had propped herself up on her arms and angled herself out of the pool towards me. She looked frustrated that I had turned away from her. I took a step back towards her and her brows furrowed a little less.

"Are you okay?" I asked as I remembered all of the kidnapping specials my mother made me sit through when I was in elementary school. "Do you need help?"

She smiled softly and shook her head.

"Does he take care of you?"

She nodded.

I couldn't help the step I took towards the pool. She smiled wider at my movement and began to sink back into the clouded water. The closer I got, the lower she sank, until I was kneeling at the edge and she had her chin resting on her arms, looking up at me.

The smile never left her face. I couldn't control the way my heart hammered away in my chest, threatening to burst through and get caught in her beautiful, sharp teeth. Did mermaids eat hearts? I'm sure I would have let her eat mine.

She leaned up again, closing the gap between our faces and opened her mouth to let out that strange noise. My eyes traveled, once again, to the slits at her throat and watched them flex as she drew breath.

"I - I don't know what you're saying," I said, because I didn't know what else to say.

She looked frustrated again for a moment, then reached out and pointed at my throat. I don't know what made me do it, but I moved forward so she could trace her fingers over where I would have had gills if I wasn't, well, human. Her fingertips were warm, like the water she was submerged in, and the path her fingers took from the side of my throat down to my collar bones felt like it was on fire.

"I don't have those," I said and realized that she must be looking for my gills. "I - "

I wasn't sure how I planned to finish that sentence. Maybe she thought all women had gills; Mr. Morrissey clearly did not have any.

Her eyes grew wide as she felt the vibrations in my throat as I spoke. I closed my eyes and savored the way the pads of her fingers felt smooth and soft. She made a noise again, but it was lower, as if it began deep in her throat. When her fingers left my throat, I waited a few tense seconds before I opened my eyes again. She had not moved and was observing me with curiosity. I wanted to say...something...anything. But when I opened my mouth, no words came out.

She reached out again, and this time wrapped her fingers around my hand. Her grip was tight, and she pulled my hands towards her. I flinched so hard I almost pulled my hands from her grip. But as I pulled back, she followed my movements, this time taking my hand far more gently. She slowly guided it back towards her to rest on her own throat.

My fingers brushed the scales that circled her gills and I remember being surprised at how smooth they were. No salt or hard water droplets clung to them to dull their shine. She let me explore the pattern of scales for a moment before taking my hand again and gently guiding my fingers to brush her delicate gills.

She opened her mouth and let out a higher pitched noise. It echoed off the green that enclosed the yard; harmonic, almost ethereal. Her gills fluttered under my fingers and she dipped her head, so it brushed against the top of my hand. She looked up at me with large eyes, they held questions I could not answer.

I hadn't heard the truck pull into the driveway. I hadn't even heard Mr. Morrissey grunt as he hauled bags of salt from the open truck bed to his driveway. It wasn't until the fence door swung open that I froze.

It happened so quickly. She raised her head and looked past me towards Mr. Morrissey, standing in the pathway to the backyard. His eyes were wide, shock that slowly morphed to horror as he saw me kneeling there. Her own eyes changed then to mirror his as if I was now a threat to her.

As she dove to safety under the murky water, her tail snapped up and caught me in the face. It stung and I fell backwards as I felt at my cheeks where the pain had blossomed. I scrambled to my feet and snatched up the ball that had started all of this. I hurried to the fence door where Mr. Morrissey was still standing, unable to fully commit to any kind of anger.

His eyes traveled to my cheek and he frowned. I placed a hand over where I had been struck and pushed past him.

"I'm sorry," I managed to say as I ran down his driveway.

I sat at my window the rest of that Summer, listening to the beautiful and chilling noises she made. I didn't have the nerve to go back there, even on late afternoons when I heard Mr. Morrissey's truck pull out of the driveway. Instead, I would look over at the scale she had left embedded in my cheek. The scale I had tucked into the corner of my mirror, that would catch the sunlight in the early morning and shine brightly.

That summer turned into fall and then winter, and I still sat at my window straining my ears for her song. As the years passed, the green canopy began to over-grow once more and her song became muffled. I ran into Mr. Morrissey in the grocery store the Summer before college.

Even three years later, I could not meet his eyes.

In the summer between sophomore and junior year of college, my girlfriend came to visit me for a week. We both had to pretend we weren't dating so my mom wouldn't make her sleep in the guest bedroom. On the last night she was there, I could hear the song drifting through my open window and I asked my girlfriend if she could hear it too. I remember she looked at me like I had a second head, so I laughed off my question and shut the window.

It wasn't until the next summer that I found myself back in that yard.

It was an unbearably hot August day; the hottest we had had in a while. The snaking vines and densely packed leaves that stood out so harshly against the houses wilted slightly, and certain leaves started to turn a bright yellow. I sat on my windowsill and listened to the quiet splashing of the water in the pool.

That was when I heard it again, clearer than I had

in years, her song was drifting up through the air and into my bedroom window. It was the first time I had heard it and not felt a twinge of sadness, not felt the desire to shut my windowpane so I could no longer listen to her ethereal sounds. I felt lightheaded, almost drunk, as her song was carried on the warm breeze.

I found myself in my backyard again, with a foam softball clutched in my hand. I contemplated it, running my fingers over the faux lacing and pressing into the softness of it as I heard Mr. Morrissey's boots slap across the pavement. When I was sure that I heard the faint sounds of his truck starting, I lobbed the softball over the fence and through the thicket of plants.

I heard it rustle everything it hit on the way down until there was a soft *thunk*.

The yard was wild. Mr. Morrissey had let the greenery spread far and wide as long as it did not impede his ability to move about the pavement near the pool. The pool itself no longer looked thickly salty; no white curled across the surface. I could see the sandy floor of the pool and the plant life that created a habitat for the mystifying creature lying at the bottom. The softball floated innocently across the water, as if it had not disturbed the pool's inhabitant.

I slipped out of my flip flops as I inched towards the pool's edge. When I reached it, I stuck my foot out and brushed my big toe across the water's surface. It was warm to the touch, and as my toe created ripples across the water, I could see her form move to flip over on the floor below.

I wished that there was still the thick salt to obscure me from her view. She rose slowly towards me as I squatted down by the edge and reached my hand out to touch the water. I only had a chance to rest my palm upon the surface when her hand shot out and gripped my wrist. She yanked me forward and I lost my footing as I plunged into the warm water.

Once I was fully submerged, I felt her let go of my wrist and I struggled to find my way to the surface with my eyes shut tight. I didn't need to open them to feel the sting of the salt beginning to build. When I finally broke the surface, I gasped for breath and coughed; a bit of water had gone up my nose and I could feel it burning in my throat.

There was a haze coating my vision that I couldn't seem to clear and when I looked around, everything had a slight ring of white surrounding it. It almost looked like a halo framing the portion of her head that was emerging out of the water.

"What was that for?" I snapped and splashed water at her. Her large eyes watched me sputter and rub at my own.

She stared at me with those large eyes and a furrowed brow, as if she was angry with me for intruding upon her once again. I swam as quickly as I could towards the shallow end of the pool. If we were going to play the "who deserved to be more mad at the other" game, then I wanted to have my feet solidly underneath me.

I heard a splash behind me as I reached the stairs, then a tug at my arm. I turned as I was pulled backwards and expected to face another angry expression. Instead, she looked panicked. It made me pause. The anger I had felt swelling within me was dampened as I searched her face.

Her grip on my arm tightened as I turned to fully look at her now.

She slowly, almost as if she was asking permission, pulled my arm to lead me back into the warm depth of the pool. I planted my feet, not letting her pull me back and as I resisted, the panic deepened in her face. I realized that maybe she hadn't been mad at me for coming back. I wasn't ready to let her submerge me again, but I relented enough to let her pull me, chest deep, into the water. Her face relaxed with each step I took.

She looked so different from the image I had in my head from that summer day all those years ago. I could see that her skin was darker from constant exposure to the sun, and the scales around her face had elongated with the pronouncement of her cheek bones. Her fingers, which had once been separate, now had a clear webbing between them; a lighter shade of purple than her scales.

I felt a fingertip gently trace the scar on my cheek. She had tilted her head in question as she observed the slightly lighter skin under her touch. I felt the water droplets she left behind roll down my face.

Her fingers left my cheek to rest under my chin and lift my head slowly. My eyes raised the rest of the way to see her gaze intently fixed upon me. I tried to swallow, to answer, but it left a dry feeling in my mouth. Now, with my eyes on her, she brushed her fingertips over the raised skin again.

"I…" I paused and chose my words carefully. "I got it that day. As you dove back under the water."

It took a few seconds as her eyes darted back and forth between mine, a frown growing on her features as she took in my words. Then her eyes widened, and she drew back her hand quickly from my face. She clutched it to her chest as if she was afraid her touch might hurt me.

"No," I said, stepping towards her; but as my feet sank into the sand, she beat her tail to push herself further from me. "No don't - "

I reached out quickly to grab at her arm the same way she had mine. I hissed in pain and drew my hand back quickly as I caught the tip of my finger on one of her scales. The cut wasn't deep, it didn't even bleed, but the salt caused it to sting. I sucked air between my teeth as I rubbed my thumb over the slit skin. I didn't notice that she moved closer again until her hands closed around mine. The webbing between her fingers was soft, almost slippery, and encased my whole hands.

She lifted my hand towards her face and scrunched up her nose as she inspected the cut from her scale. I bit my lip to stop the smile from spreading across my face. Then, slowly, she brought my finger close, closed her eyes, and pressed her lips to the split skin.

A heat prickled at my skin, hot and uncomfortable and not caused by the beating of the sun or the temperature of the water. It started in my cheeks and spread to my ears, down my neck, across my chest. She pulled away and let go of my hand. Her eyes were brighter now and I let my own trace over the features of her face again before they lingered on her lips.

I moved closer, and this time she did not back away. She drifted forward through the water until we were almost nose to nose.

"Can I?" My mouth still felt dry. She was not the first woman I had kissed, and she would not be the last. I still couldn't help the way my pulse quickened under her soft gaze. "Can I kiss you?"

She raised her eyebrows at me. It didn't seem like a question, but she gave no answer either. I shut my mouth quickly, having lost some confidence then.

"I'm sorry, I shouldn't have - "

But she silenced me by laying a finger on my lips. She tapped her finger there once, twice, then placed that same finger on her own lips. She tapped her finger again and I understood.

"Yes," I said, and nodded to make sure she understood.

She smiled. A smile that reached her eyes and bared teeth to me that were sharper than mine, but not sharp enough that I worried about my tongue if it was to meet hers. She nodded and closed the distance between us so our noses were touching now. I giggled at her playfulness and raised my own hands to cup her face.

She moved forward, and I met her halfway this time. It was gentle at first, both of us cautiously claiming the other's lips. I could only assume that she had never kissed anyone before, so I understood her hesitance, her hands tentatively gripped my waist, then pulled me closer. What I didn't understand was why my own hands started to tremble against her skin. How my breath shook when we finally broke apart.

I've never forgotten the brightness of her eyes as she smiled wide at me, or the way she sounded as she laughed. She kissed me sweetly, once, twice, three more times before I held her face close again and kissed her deeply. My own laughter bubbled up in my throat as I sank backwards into the water, her body followed mine without breaking our kiss.

Over the years I have listened for her song whenever I've returned home. For the first few, no matter how many women lovingly ran their fingers over my scar, it had always called to me; strong and loud. When I met my wife, it began to dull. Now, I no longer hear it through the thick canopy I can still see from my childhood bedroom.

I still keep her scale tucked into the corner of my mirror.

Selected Poems
by Kathy Kremins

Johnny Boy

My mother's mother died
when she was eight, and
for those next ten years,
she cut turf, milked cows,
cooked and cleaned
for my grandfather, isolated
in the bogs of Roscommon.

What would she know about
the small love of a child and mother?
She lived for the big love
of her Johnny. She struggled
to save some of it for me,
a clone of my father, but a girl,
who failed at girling,
with my torn jeans, skinned knees,
short hair, muddy hands.

As the Parkinson's slid
into dementia, I slid
into Johnny on my daily visits,
where we would sit for tea at Grunings
soon after she arrived in Newark.
I would court her in my father's way,
and she fell in love with me,
living beyond her prognosis.
Call it grace.

Ode to Sandy

A low whoosh hummed steadily as if hovering
rather than the usual cadence of a summer
storm bloated with lightning and thunder.
But this was late October with winds from
a wrong season approaching. Hours later,
once the rains began, the moon, full and bright,
somewhere in the clouds threw a fierce boom of
unrelenting air and water at the ocean and sand,
propelling them in vicious swirls, unpredictable
patterns. I buried my head in old pictures of a
drowning beach, waiting for the silence of the dying.

Self-Portrait as Estuary,
or Newark Bay Meditation

Here is the end of longing
in the thousand lives of my body
of waters where my rivers
with their tributaries and intimate streams
wandering neighborhood yards meet
the Atlantic with its salty tongue
embracing my cold freshness.
People call me names: bay, lagoon,
sound, or insult me with slough.
My water moves in continuous
motion so I don't forget where
I land. There is no place there.
I live in the detritus of the daily,
the uncertainty, contradiction,
complexity of ocean waves and winds
with only the tides and returning birds
to lend some ritual to the ever-evolving,
embattled geography with mud and sand
shifting and re-directing in this confluence
of pause, let go, embrace, pause. let go,
embrace. I hold onto nothing.

Wild West

As if a Jersey girl in Utah wasn't wild enough
said girl kissing her first girlfriend, first love

on the edge of Inspiration Point, crimson
hoodoos rising spire-like across

Bryce Canyon at sunset, days later
balanced at sunrise at Sunrise Point

stretched into space looking for the best angle
leaning over the jagged crags to catch a photo

shot after red-rising shot, rapid-fire as I totter
slip, trip - now in my slow-motion memory -

reach back with my left hand toward earth
drop the Nikkon from my right hand, tumbles

into the abyss of the gorge. I still feel your fingers
dig into my shoulder, pulling me back from uncertain death

the sound of the crashing camera echoes like my bones
certainly not the last time you saved me from me.

A Vesper Of Sorts

The asymmetrical plot of land along the North Branch of the Raritan
onced mined for iron, resisted the digging. But you wanted a garden
and I wanted you happy. So we dug and heaved and split and threw
into the river bed all the unburied stones. You sank four stakes,
expertly measured with your artist eye, marked by string, a sacred
ground. Seven years that garden thrived in the shadow of the
bamboo stand and on midsummer nights, the fireflies in a
synchronized pulse, illuminated snap peas, squash, cucumbers,
carrots, tomatoes, Kohlrabi, lettuce, radish, green beans, peppers.
We drank red wine, listening to the music of the humming water,
munching snap peas, barefooted, with shoots of light darting through
the trees, a spiderweb spotlighted, kisses, a vesper of sorts on
consecrated land.

Off Season
by Scott Napp

I do hate when Visitors call my home a ghost town with such disdain. Every September the 1st, it seems the winds shift and suddenly the Visitors look at it as if it were disposable. Begging your pardon, but for some of us, the Cape is always a ghost's town. Just because a few of you show up when the weather is warm you think, what, we just hibernate the rest of the year? Hold our metaphoric breath for the day when you'll return to spill your beer on our freshly polished floors, drip your ice cream on the tablecloths and shed sand all over pressed sheets? No sir! We have our own sizable population of permanent residents here, thank you very much. And there are more of us than you realize. More than most of you see. Definitely more than most of you would care to believe.

I should know these things. I've been a Local for 142 years.

What would you know, anyway? You're just another one of them. Passed your money over to the innkeeper, drop your bags all over my rooms and act like it's your own personal castle. What, you've never thought of privacy? Poking around wherever you like, shouting for me, shouting for the others. It's enough to fray the nerves.

Oh, sure, check in the old coal room in the basement. That's where I'd want to spend time immemorial hiding. Truly, you lot have some strange ideas about a Local's day-to-day activities. I'll give you a tiny hint: the Long Gone crowd never was much interested in spending our days hiding in drafty attics or contorted in crawl spaces.

Did you plug cotton in your ears? Why do you keep waving your lights about under the bed? What possible purpose would I have under there? I'm not a child playing hide and seek. If you want to do that, talk with the Sherman boy over on Jackson Street. Come to think of it, I take back that crack about the crawlspace. Poor chap froze solid in one of those. Not that you'd know it, as he's been dodging about the traffic there for nigh on a century ever since. The bed and breakfast guests always have such a fright when they catch a glimpse of him. The lad always looks like the cat that caught the canary afterwards. He's a chatterbox; try and corner him, perhaps he'll tell tales for you?

I see you're traveling with quite a few stories on your computer about this neighborhood! Well, that does make me feel a bit like a high-falutin' muck-a-muck to garner such treatment.

What, you didn't think I knew about your fancy laptop?

Look, some of us here may have shuffled off the mortal coil but that doesn't mean we haven't been paying attention. Time is in no short supply for us anymore, so we do enjoy listening in as you create your new phrases and change your words. Some I adopted myself! Others...well, you have become a bit more vulgar to my liking. So yes, I've looked on in awe as you flew higher and higher in the sky with your airplanes and your phones went from wood and wire to wristwatches. You proudly present your shiny toys only to replace them with fancier widgets when it strikes your fancy. In my day you wouldn't be caught out with a dress above your ankles but now you'd be hard pressed to find a woman in July who wasn't wearing naught but a few stitches. Shops change ownership by the season in some places, while other houses have been in the hands of the same family for nearly as long as I've been here.

That's the price you pay, being in a town like our beloved Cape May. You become accustomed to the balance of the temporary and the perennial. If you lose your focus, sometimes it's hard to remember if you're wandering a street at night in 2021 or 1891. You hear the clip clop of horse beats and you think it's someone home from work in the fields. But turn a corner without thinking and you'll see an electric car whoosh past you like a bat out of hell.

Have you ever felt that way about the fragility of time? Have you ever been so lost in thought that the air around you seems to part like curtains on a stage and for a moment, you could be strolling through what was? Or have those gadgets ensnared you in the hold of the present?

Who am I joshing? You're not listening. I see you've found another half-cocked story from one of the Visitors! I remember him. He was half-bombed and thus must be more relevant to pay attention to rather than listen to a primary source right next to you.

Oh no. No, stop looking at that story, it's utter bunk! You don't think I'm the widow in that story, do you? Don't you think that there would be newspaper stories written about something as awful as a hanging suicide in a town this small? You seemed so much smarter than the others who have come calling to this house. Besides, that woman they're describing is Miss Stone from three houses down and she's a nasty old crone!

Have I been known to knock things over? A touch, a tough, I do confess. Only when you raise my hackles, though! I just can't stand when people try to remodel this house! Its beauty is of the classical variety! If burning out a few bulbs and knocking over some cheap china will stop the family from putting linoleum down over hardwood, can you fault me for my actions? That's as far as I go, though. If you want flying cutlery, go tell Miss Stone her husband's been lost at sea for 173 years. See how that does you...

Sea travel. Do any of you even travel by sea anymore? I never much cared for it in my corporeal days. Or any travel, really. Then, as now, my heart beats for this seaside town. And while my heart may be dust, that fullness it once contained has remained a part of me, and thus I remain here. The sea gets into your lungs and makes it nigh impossible to wish to be anywhere else. In the spring, the whole town's a riot of flowery aromas mixed with the salt air. When the sun's blaze heats the sands in summer, nothing is more comforting than the cool breeze of the surf. Sing a sad song of the season's change, for it's always sad to see death's hold on nature, but it is a wonder to behold when the leaves become as vibrant and fiery as the flames that nearly consumed the town whole once.

Winter, though, is when the town becomes The Locals' again. We can stroll our streets without worrying about scaring one of you to an early graveyard appointment. The cars and trucks and boats are scattered to the four winds. Bed and breakfasts lock up for the season. "See you in the spring!" they post on painted wooden signs outside their doors and in their yards. Neptune casts a gray pallor over his aquatic empire and with the icy cutting feel in the air, few wander to the sands to gaze upon it. The few Visitors who come for holiday cheer in December flee quickly to warm homes far away.

Suddenly we're free to visit friends from the days of our youths, should they have chosen to delay The Great Move. Homes that we once took tea in or played ball outside of or simply passed time in are welcome to us once more.

The streets become somber and still. Young people looking to neck with someone they fancy have concluded their summer trysts. Old folk looking to stretch aching legs and backs have retreated to warmer climates. Pools are covered, fountains shut off and the tour ponies are safe in their stables. The bandstand is left lonesome, glazed by icy streaks, waiting for a new season's crowds.

I like to visit the bandstand. There's something oddly comforting about people gathering to listen to songs that were written long before their birth by people who died generations before their children crawled.

Did...did you really just ask me how I died? Sir! If you think it's ungentlemanly to ask a woman their age, how indignant do you think I should be about being asked something as momentous as my spiritual exit?

For that, I'm draining the battery on your computer. It's the least you deserve.

Oh. Did I hurt your feelings, doing that? Well maybe next time don't try to incite a spirit. We're still human, you know.

For your information, no, I don't remember dying. I don't think any of us really do. Maybe the moments leading up to it but...be it the Almighty's kindness or a safety function for our minds, we lose that final memory. Some of us were lucky and died warm in bed, with long years behind us. Others, such as I, had abbreviated spells upon this globe, our endings abrupt.

Judging by your notes, I see you've already sought out young Master Earl by the waterfront. Do you think he truly wants to remember the moment of his passing, with an accidental shotgun blast to his face? Of course not.

I do feel a mite bit of shame telling you this story when it's not my own. But I do so in the hopes that you hear me. We were here. Then we were not. And then we found ourselves back again with no comprehension of how. Some of us have not had the easiest time adjusting to these new circumstances. Is there anything more human than disorientation? Think on that, the next time you try to "conjure a spirit" or challenge us to "show ourselves."

Is that...it that a picture of me? How did you...

It has been many, many years since I've seen myself. I'd almost forgotten...and oh. Oh there is that dress, that damnable dress. I knew I was not meant for such frilly frivolities but...just once I wanted to have something to show I could be a lady of style and grace. But that dress...

Listen once, young searcher, for I'm not likely to speak on it again.

I don't know how it is that I got back here. I was locked from my room and, being alone with no other alternative, I took to a window and attempted to shimmy my way around the awning to a balcony adjacent to my room's window. Having prepared to meet my young beau Daniel, I was clad in that very dress you see in that photo. I was told by my friends that he'd likely become undone to see his rough-and-tumble lass in such finery. This need to impress became my undoing, sadly. The last thing I remember thinking was that my dress would not allow enough flexibility to get a leg over the railing...and then Gravity reached out its mighty hand and pulled me close.

There are days where I wonder how Daniel's life unfurled after my Departure. Perhaps his great-grandchildren have run past this house, never knowing their inherited connection to this place. To my sad ending.

As I grew accustomed to my new shapeless existence, I found that time had marched forward, and entire neighborhoods had been lost to great fires and fierce floods. I suppose this is the way of things for a community so close to the shore but for a community that had been immutable for so long, it was jarring when I "awoke" to see such progress.

I don't really know why it took me so long to reappear. It was a slow process, not unlike learning one's alphabet or taking one's early shaking steps. Over time, I found myself back in the old inn that my parents once rented to Visitors. Father had passed years before my worldly departure in the War, but I could not find him in the house or wandering about the town. Nor could I find Mother, who had passed only a year before, lay low by cholera.

My parents, like so many of our friends and neighbors, had been drawn to the light of the spiritualists. Mother held strong to the belief that Father had not simply fallen at Bull Run but instead had ventured on to the next stop on the line, to a serene land where he could meet us again. I hope this belief gave her peace when she too crossed that ethereal sea. Perhaps they will be there whenever I finally wade through those waters myself.

But I can't bear to leave my beautiful home. Not when there are so many new things to learn and to see and to do. When you all read books, I can follow along without worrying about needing rest for the next day's work. And with radio? Television? The Internet? My thirst for knowledge has only grown. Your world takes for granted the ability to learn on a whim.

Take, for example, the fact that I am trying to contextualize the scope of life beyond your current pane of existence while you, an enlightened modern soul, are considering looking at the video of a talking cat your friend sent you.

Matilda is going to never let me hear the end of this. For a housekeeper who died in the 30s, she sure has picked up a lot of modern psychology from you people. She said it would be a mistake trying to reason with a Visitor. I replied that with all of the advances in technology, with the ability to access the totality of human knowledge with the click of a button, that you'd have to be capable of grasping what I had to say.

And here you are, taking a picture of yourself in the dark without a flash.

This was a mistake.

Oh, your attention is back on me now? No, I'm afraid I'm not ready to continue the conversation. Do you ever wonder why you get ghostly names on your recordings that don't match with your facts? It's not because your notes are inaccurate or your recording muddied.

It's because you were irksome and as a jest, we sometimes say we're someone else, just to play hob with your research. Some people, like Grandpa Albert on Lafayette Street, prefer to whisper just quietly enough that you can hear him but not enough to understand him. You should hear him chortling after you leave the room in a snit. The man loved good wine, good cheese and a good laugh while alive. He's fine with only being able to have one of them now.

I'm sure you've been to the Emerald Glen. Despite the fact that it is devoid of any actual permanent spiritual residents, you all persist in examining it. Weary from your paranormal playtime, you gather round the stone fireplace for hours to escape the night's chills. You tell stories and cuddle together and watch the dancing of the flames. You admire the archaic feeling it gives you, the feel of something your ancestors did. You never notice the story in front of your face.

The fireplace you admire? It is bolstered by broken tombstones. Yes, Visitor, you were warmed by a hearth constructed by stones bearing the name of this town's long forgotten natives and lodgers. These final markers were buried by rising tides and the Atlantic's mighty storms, washed and re-washed to the point where even granite-carved names began to disappear. Rock quarries were too far to reach, and necessity required innovation so your ancestors used what they could to build their dream homes.

The stones' names, barely seen by the keenest eye, grow fainter every year.

Someone carved those names by hand. And both stone-carver and stone-recipient have been left to antiquity. But for the sharp of eye and quick of wit, maybe their stories will be recovered and told once more. That's a kind of partial immortality, isn't it?

A week ago, I was called on by my friend Elizabeth, who I met decades ago while wandering through my favorite pub, jostling glasses for fun. She and her husband once owned a small grocery and passed during a flu epidemic. Lovely souls, always watching out for the children who come to town. They've enjoyed watching their descendants grow but most have moved away and now are wondering if it's time to let go of this place and leave too.

I haven't seen them since.

So when you ask me, "Why haven't you moved on." it's because I'm really not ready to! You can say it's unfinished business, but I think of it as an unfinished vacation. I worked hard in life and never accomplished half of what I sought to do by my end. So I'm staying until I'm done enjoying myself. I wish to learn. I wish to laugh. As long as I feel love for the sunrise over the ocean in the morning, I may never leave.

You're packing up your cameras? I suppose you haven't gotten much material to work with. I'm never sure how much your little microphones can pick up, even if I shout. Ah well, it's all for the best. I do need to check in on my cats.

Oh yes, your cat and dogs and birds and rabbits? Some of them stick around too. Those times where you trip over nothing? Sometimes it's a bad step. Other times it's just one of your old friends coming back to show affection.

Before you shut down your microphone, can I make a recommendation?

Stop looking for people like me. Find love, have adventures, get hurt-- just don't try being a third-floor daredevil act like I did--and just...live. Don't obsess over our stories.

Go create your own.

Selected Poems
● by Jimmy Cullen

Introduction

Curtain, Roses
Bedroom door closes
Smile fades
Shoulders sag
He thinks "this is a drag"

Preps for bed
Takes his meds
Says his prayers
Anyone there?

Eyes are heavy
Moods unsteady
Wishes for sleep
A quieting peace

No longer afraid of what is to come
Knowing things will return
To their respective places

Eyelids close
Deep breaths follow
This boy dreams
In technicolor

The Confessional

Will you forgive me?
I asked
Alone in my chambers
On the floor
Fetal position
Under the moonlight

I've asked for forgiveness
Too many times now
I've lost count
No answer has been given
What now?

I know you can hear me
What can you do
It's my cross that I have to bear
For the rest of my life

People claim it was the devil
That drove me to it
It was my last resort
Couldn't carry the weight of it
Had to get away from it

So I ask this question
Again
Can you forgive me?
I can't forgive myself

Neon Does Not Fade

You're my last addiction
I can't give you up
So sweet
It ignites me
It exhilarates me
Realization sinks in
This isn't permanent
Only the relapse
Can I rise above
I demand it
God has other plans
As I shine
I fade
I wave goodbye
Only to say hello
Can you hear me

Golden Duckling

Finally it's my chance
The sun feels so good
My eyes have adjusted

I can feel everything
The golden child has risen
I've been waiting for this moment
So long

No one can out beat
Perfection
No one can outrun
My wrath
I'm unpredictable
Omnipresent

This ugly duckling needs me
It's all about survival
Me against him
Me against the world

Alas, my time on earth is waning
I will be back again
It's time for this ugly duckling
To take control again

Finale

At the end of this inspiration
The muse has gone
Left only me
I know it will return
The question is
When?

Shall I end on something nice
Should I end it in obscurity
Would it be best to stay moody
Or better to quit while ahead

I will write again when I'm ready
Until then
Know this
I will always find expression in words

**New Jersey in ●
photographs (part 2)**
by Gaveth Pitterson

Longing for summer and the beach.

Skipping rocks on the lake. Did you see that!

Silhouette in the shade.

Saturday afternoon drive on a road less travelled.

Two shall become one. Camping with my love.

Birdie in the sand.

Stay Salty

Leisurely strolls on the beach are priceless.

Glorious sunset. Life is good.

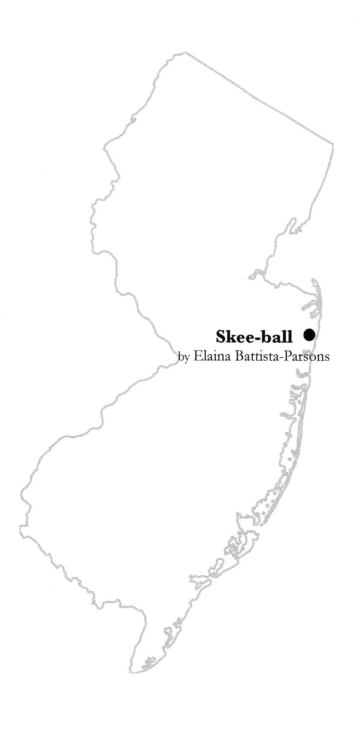

Skee-ball ●
by Elaina Battista-Parsons

I miss Raven and our getaways. I've been revising my horror novel for weeks, buried in the trenches of theme and plot, trying to get every aspect to attach itself to the other so that the reader won't want to stop reading. As I sip my local coffee brew in the comfort of my tangerine desk chair, I crave twelve-year-old type fun. No deep point of view nuances, no dialogue tags. Simple amusement. My body, heart, and mind long for some time with Raven. I text her my dramatic wishes, she gives me an eye roll emoji, and honks in front of my apartment within twenty minutes. Top down on her powder blue VW bug, sunglasses too big for her head, and windblown salty brown hair. Perfection. July is our month. July is the Jersey shore's favorite child.

We agree on the Heights—take your pick of three arcades, fully equipped with scratchy accordion music, pizza, and original 1971 carpets. Most of us, young and old, prefer Cora's Cove because it has the most colorful and vintage of carousels. It also has Bathtub Bubbles, and well, it's a rad game. You have to aim your water pistol at the bullseye until the half-naked kid's old fashioned clawfoot bathtub fills up. It takes precise water gun aim, so being a local, you have an unfair advantage to practice year-round. Yes, I'm twenty-four, and I have no shame about being proficient in Bathtub Bubbles.

After Memorial Day, finding parking in the Heights is a hassle, because no local will pay $20 for the all-day lot. Our town is eternally swamped with out-of-towners from late May until local summer begins after Labor Day. Out-of-towners with their excessive posses are in full effect as we circle and square the streets for a spot. Raven's arm air glistens in the sun. "You smell great, Neen," Raven says as she waves on anxious pedestrians to cross.

"It's called coffee breath, but thanks," I say. I apply my pomegranate lipgloss and flatten my unruly eyebrows. Writers named Nina Renaro have no time to worry about waxing their brows where they're this close to finishing their third manuscript.

Finally, Raven yelps, "YEAH! Front and center!" It is lucky timing, and we're grateful on a scorcher like today to park so close. We have no plans to swim, so relief will eventually look like Lucky Lenny's Lemonade with an avalanche of ice and tickles of lemon zest.

It's 6 p.m., and the sun still beats down on the greasy boardwalk. My dad's Mecca, Teak Barn Steakhouse, dominates the air—sausage and peppers on a hard Italian roll. A whole lotta grease, and tangles of grilled onions. He lives for it. And will die by it too.

We take our time getting to Cora's. I'm in the mood for throwing darts at droopy, half-filled balloons. Honestly, I am actually dying to play some Skee-Ball. "How's the novel coming?" she asks.

"Meh." I mean, it's an accurate response.

Raven reads my mind, because as soon as we get to Cora's, she snakes through the arcade, past the prize counter, and grabs two Skee-Ball alleys for us. Clink, Clink. Two quarters each, per round.

The 9 balls zoom down, signaling it's the player's time to focus, swing back an arm, flick the wrist, release, and check your luck. Those tiny circle slots on the upper sides of the cage are super tough to nail, but once in a while, you get it right in the 50-point pocket! I don't know how to put that kind of satisfaction into words.

We play four rounds each, and our scores match up pretty well. We snap our grasshopper green prize tickets out of the slots and shove them in our totes. Today's earnings will get us no more than a few cheap plastic boomerangs. Skee-Ball is a game of redemption, but the big prizes require loyalty and patience.

The thunder of the roll and the flick of the brown balls (some tan and coffee swirled) builds up an appetite. Santino's Pizza is a four-minute walk up the boards. Diamonds, blue glitter, and red stardust fill the sky. The pop and fizzle sends shivers up my spine, as Raven smiles and nods. The purple teardrop fireworks are everything. Friends who-could-be-more don't always need to talk. Words might break the beauty. Silence in friendship is underrated. Being an adult who lives near the heartbeat of summer is underrated.

Selected Poems
by Eileen Mueller

My Dear Gray-Green-y Atlantic

Today I came to you in a fat-wheeled
rolling chair, down a long twisting ramp.
It was a strange and precarious journey,
and my husband had to take many rests.

You smell so good to me, the roll, and shush,
and slap of your waves. I take joy in the tiny people,
dipping, hopping, and rising on them, or caught
in the fizz of their breakings. The air is delicious.

I feel opened and less weary now, watching
you surge and retreat, the same wet flowerings
that woke me, now alive in wet-suited kids riding
boogie boards, ceaselessly wiping out and starting
over.

How they fan out over your surface, loners all,
until the right wave swoops them up, turns
them into a flock, riding in unison all the way
to the sand, crying out as if they were gulls.

Nacre

The way a life builds, she thinks,
layer upon layer, each one adding
strength, making the soul
more luminous, and loved
ones more beautiful.

The way the years
and their experiences
can break or fortify
a marriage, eat away
at love's body, or
smooth out memory's
rough edges to protect
its soft tissue core.

The way pain and grief
change color, as the
angle of vision shifts,
the way damaging debris
disappears beneath resilience,
and forgiveness turns
trouble iridescent.

Not so much a miracle, she thinks,
that the shell around them is still intact,
as a mystery, tied to these trips to this
outermost place, to get our bearings,
soften, release, solidify, forget.

Out The Front Window
in Medford Lakes

A little girl in a leopard print jacket roars by
driving a pink battery-powered jeep, followed,
twenty feet behind, by a tired old looking
grandpa, pushing a baby in a stroller.

Just so, back and forth they go many times,
insistently writing and rewriting themselves
across the page of this early morning,
the plastic wheels growling out their advent
well before I can see anything, signaling me
to watch and wait for another sight of her,
shooting like an arrow across my window,
head up and full of certainty, plunging
in a straight line toward the future.

How determined we are, when we first
start out on this recursive journey
through what turns out to be a finite life,
with its lessons that repeat and repeat,
its foreshadowings, its countable
epiphanies, its limited opportunities.

Adults let us go on believing
a universe of possibility lies ahead.
We can be whatever we want to be.
How blissful, the look on their faces,
as they watch us inscribe our singularity
on the present. Though they can't

wholeheartedly do likewise,
how very much they want us to press on.

Wren

sitting atop a fence post,
beak full of grass and down.
At the window, I watch,
as she tilts her head
this way, that way,
her black eyes
scanning the ground
and then the air between us
in little sweeps, careful
not to show exactly where
she's building her nest.

The world's a dangerous place.

Quick as a sigh, she flies off,
as a big squirrel muscles up the post,
and sits where she did a second ago,
to gnaw on a juicy acorn.

She swoons nearby, then drops
at a blue jay's thud on the roof,
its hungry cry cutting us both.
And then resumes her task,
as soon as they're gone.

I watch as she carries on,
eggs already forming,
calling her to this
ritual of hatchlings,

their cries, their cries,
their hunger to exist.

To A Drunken Girl at
the Jersey Shore

I've seen you before, heard your hoarse voice
rise above the others', watched you bop to the beat,
tan in your black bikini, tossing your dry yellow hair,
teetering forward, wading into the surf to take a leak,
or to rinse the sand from an almost empty gallon of Wild
Turkey, then pour what's left into your can of Diet Coke.

But today you've turned comedienne, following an older woman,
as she walks the sand, and climbs onto the boardwalk, holding
your hands up as if you have a belly big as hers is, rocking
from side to side, like an elephant at the circus, and this,
the nerve of it, moves the boys, you party with,
to hoot, applaud, and slap you five in disbelief.

I wonder if you know that when the fires finally sputtered
out, at the World Trade Center, when all hope was lost
for survivors, and the digging began, there were jewels
nestled in the dust, jewels that once were window glass,
young women stared through as they sat at their desks,
sleepy-eyed on that particular sunny morning. Glass
transformed by calamity, hatred crushed and made
molten, burnished, and condensed into loveliness.
Glass babies calved by a massive glacier of grief.

Life writes on you, you know: tattoos collect as you age,
feel heavy as a suit of armor you never asked for.
All the partying, the parched and bloated aftermaths,
the losses, the cruelties, etch themselves into your brain,

your liver, your hair and skin. Oh, but keep drinking and
running wild while you can. Even beautiful legs wear down,
feet widen, toes become clawed and ugly, soon, you look
like a house on chicken feet. You'll find yourself sitting
in some local bar, wracking your brain for quips to
throw back at the men who like to taunt you,
sensing your desperation. Maybe some young
girl gets up, and mimes a big belly behind you.

The glacier's relentless, chasing every one of us.
Okay, I'm being too hard on you. Consider it ice
in a sweating glass of bourbon, glacial in its (s)melting,
while Alice slips through the mirror and never comes back.
Put a shot glass to your eye to distort the view, if you must,
but find the jewel of your kindness. I think it's blue

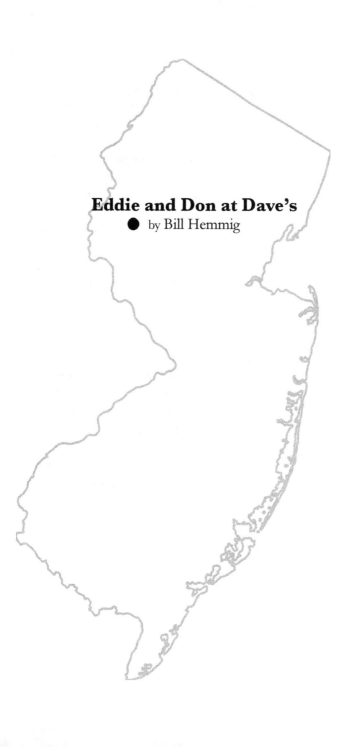

Eddie and Don at Dave's

● by Bill Hemmig

For his whole life, whenever Eddie expected to see a thing but it wasn't there, for just a split second he'd see it anyway. And that's what happened this morning. He came around the corner from the back of Chris's Citgo and there was his pickup at the pump where he left it and then it just wasn't. Three tons of metal plus his crap in the back, not to mention Amy—it all just vanished while he watched.

Eddie looked up and down the street but no cherry red Ram. Where would Amy go with it? He ran through the morning so far. They left from her apartment after spending the night together. He didn't tell her what his plans were—he liked to make little surprises, and since her apartment and her car were crammed with stuffed animals he figured a trip to the county zoo might be a nice one so he went for it. He promised her breakfast first and was going to take her to his regular diner up on Route 9, where no ex-girlfriends worked right now. But first he stopped at Chris's Citgo. He did need to fill the truck but more than that he needed to empty himself, and while his relationship with Amy seemed solid, it was far from the stage where he'd be comfortable smelling up her bathroom.

Somebody back in the garage was playing Aerosmith. Steven Tyler just saw his last girlfriend somewhere and he's a mess and she looks like she doesn't have a care in the world. Did she forget something and drive back to her place? He stopped to pull his phone out of his pocket but then realized that he left it in the truck. Two cars had pulled up to other pumps and their occupants looked blankly at

Eddie. Maybe he should just wait here until she comes back. He noticed a long blue cloth draped over the pump where the pickup had been, like the pump was out of order. But it wasn't out of order—he left Tyler Caldwell filling the pickup when he went around back to use the men's room. He noticed the people in the cars still looking at him and he realized that nobody was helping them. Maybe they thought that he was the attendant and were starting to wonder about him. What happened to Tyler?

He looked at the gas pump again, and the cloth over it. He squinted and he saw on the cloth the Citgo badge and the pocket with the short word starting with a capital T sewn onto it.

That's not a cloth. One of the drivers punched his horn.

That's the coveralls Tyler Caldwell had on.

And Tyler, Eddie's pickup, and Eddie's girlfriend were all gone.

The horn again. Chris Caldwell came out of the garage. He walked right past Eddie and toward the car with the horn. He called Tyler's name. Eddie needed to be noticed.

"Where's your kid?" he shouted.

Chris looked at him like he'd just now noticed he was there, which was probably true. Chris dated Eddie's older sister when they were in high school, so he'd known Eddie for years but had a habit of looking past him. Chris called his son's name again.

"Where is your fucking kid?" Eddie repeated.

Chris was looking around. "What's it to you?" he mumbled, and started off toward the side of the building. Eddie lunged at the gas pump and grabbed at the coveralls. He reached Chris in three strides and spun him around. Chris was a strong man but Eddie was stronger. He held the embroidered pocket inches from Chris's face.

"This was on your kid," he growled. "Now this is here but your kid's not and my pickup's not and my girlfriend's gone."

Chris stared at him. "What?" He tried to shake Eddie's hand from his shoulder.

"What do you not get here, man?" Eddie tightened his grip and he got a sudden image of them. Amy in her pink shorts and that blouse with the little flowers. The skinny blond kid who works for his dad on weekends while he commutes to college sitting next to her in Eddie's Ram in nothing but undershorts and sneakers. He's driving. Was she kidnapped?

"Your goddamned kid stole my truck and my girlfriend!" he shouted. His right hand was already a fist within the coveralls and the coveralls met Chris's face hard. Chris's fists flailed out but Eddie's other hand jumped to the back of Chris's head and held it there and he punched him again. Chris got heavier and Eddie knew he didn't need to defend himself. He kept driving the coveralls into Chris's face. Steven Tyler wailed. Two mechanics from the garage and one of the motorists came and tried to pull Eddie off of Chris. Eddie could have fought them off but Chris had become dead weight and so Eddie let him drop and allowed himself to be pulled away. The image came back. Who takes their clothes off to kidnap somebody? Now Amy's behind the wheel and Tyler's in the passenger seat. Amy's right hand rests on his naked, hairless thigh. She has to look forward to drive but he's looking at her and they're both grinning—no, laughing—heading up Route 9 and away from this. Away from him. His head was hot and he felt like his skull was going to pop and everything was fuzzy and red, like he had blood in his eyeballs. That bitch. He had to go. That fucking bitch.

One of the guys had gotten between Chris and the ground. Eddie tore away from the other two and when they lunged at him he threw up his hands and backed away. He had to get away from this. Four months. Four months he was with Amy, and she made him wait three before sleeping with him. He thought she might be the one. He thought she wanted that. He had plans. He had all kinds of plans. Then you stop somewhere to take a crap, just to be fucking thoughtful, and...

He turned his back on Chris's Citgo and walked down Bayshore. Nobody would follow him; they had Chris and the station to take care of and he was too strong. He just walked at what was probably a regular pace but how could anybody know what was regular? The sun was warm and there were no clouds at all. It was a beautiful day. A warm, sunny Saturday in May, one of those rare days when it's like summer but not summer and the shore isn't swarming with vacationers and you can actually go someplace. He had plans. The diner, and the zoo. She liked animals. She was hot and she was nice and she liked the things he did and he thought she might be the one. Where was he going? He knew that he knew where he was going but he couldn't think of what it was.

It was only three blocks down on the same side of the same street. Not far enough but what choice did he have? As soon as he saw it he knew where he was going. It was one piece of a half-block concrete strip mall. Ten AM and the four neon signs in the window were on—Miller, Coors, Heineken, and Budweiser—and there was the sign above the door.

Dave's.

He had to talk to Dave.

Eddie and Dave had been best friends since elementary school. Dave was shorter and kind of heavy and not very physical and did better in school, so Eddie was Dave's protector and Dave was there when Eddie freaked out or got into trouble. Dave should have gone to college, and did for a year, but then his dad passed away and left nothing but this bar and a lot of debt, so Dave came home and kept the bar and got married and had kids and this was his place. Dave was always here. Eddie was here when he didn't have to be anywhere else. For more than half his life, whenever he freaked out or got into trouble, and every time he got dumped, Eddie came here to talk to Dave.

He pulled the door open and started shouting. It was always pretty dark in Dave's, and so stumbling in from the sunlight Eddie could see almost nothing. But there, across the room, behind the bar and silhouetted against the dim reflections from liquor bottles, was the outline of Dave's rounded upper body, and the slightest glint off of his glasses when he looked toward the door, and off the top of his balding head.

"That bitch! That fucking…Dave, man, a beer and a shot of Daniels man you have to talk to me!"

And then it happened again. Eddie reached the bar and his eyes got used to the darkness a little and Dave disappeared. Just like that. Just like the truck. Dave disappeared and instead there was a what, a who?—a strange woman was behind the bar. Eddie stopped mid-expletive and just stood there.

She was probably forty or so like him and her hair was tied back. She wasn't wearing glasses. She'd taken a step back but came forward again and smiled nervously. She asked him what kind of beer he'd like. He'd never seen her before in his life.

What the fuck. Eddie looked around. There was nobody else in the bar. "Where's Dave?"

She reached out as if to comfort his right arm but thought better of it. "He had an accident. I mean he's going to be okay, but he was washing glasses and there was a broken one and he didn't know and he cut his hand pretty bad. Too bad to drive so he called his wife and she took him to the ER." Dave and Cindy lived almost around the corner. Cindy was a substitute teacher and must have been at home today.

Eddie's head was hot again. He could feel the walls going up inside his skull. He turned from the woman and stepped toward the door. He had to talk to Dave. Fuck. The hospital was a good ten minutes north doing seventy on the Parkway without traffic and he didn't have his wheels. Or even his phone.

The woman spoke behind him. "A shot of Jack Daniels, right?" And he heard the familiar plonk of a shot glass set down on varnished wood.

He needed something else, too.

He turned back and stepped up to the bar. He picked up the shot and downed it and shut his eyes. He felt the warmth crawl down his throat. And waited to feel that first detonation. She asked him again what kind of beer he wanted. It distracted him and he missed the moment. He opened his eyes and she was in his face.

"Who are you?" he sneered.

She smiled. "My name's Donna." She extended her hand for a shake. "My friends call me Don." He did not accept her handshake, and instead set the empty shot glass down on the bar.

"Beer?" she asked.

When he had to talk to Dave, the drinking part was inseparable from the talking part. At least he could have a beer while he figured out what to do.

"Sam Adams on tap" he said, inflected to let her know that if she had any right to be behind that bar she wouldn't have to ask.

She grabbed a glass and it took her a moment to locate the right tap. Between that and filling the glass, she seemed to decide that she needed to fill the silence too.

"I came in to ask about the help-wanted sign in the window." Eddie didn't know there was a sign in the window, but it wasn't unusual for Dave to be looking for help. People came and went. "We were in the middle of the interview when he cut himself. He was going to just close up, but I said I could watch the place until he got back."

That was weird. Dave was a hell of a nice guy but

he wasn't a moron and she was a total stranger.

"I guess it's a good sign that he trusted me," she added, as if guessing Eddie's thoughts. She set his beer down on the bar and drew closer to him.

"You said you needed to talk to Dave. Well, I'm a pretty good listener."

Fuck this. Eddie grabbed the beer and was going to take it to his usual stool near the far end of the bar. But he decided to send a stronger message, veered off and walked away to a table along the wall near the jukebox, where he sat down with his back to the bar. He had to think. He had to talk to Dave.

"Seriously," the woman said from behind the bar. "If something's on your mind the best thing to do is to just get it out there."

Dave was at the hospital and Eddie had no car. Who could he get a car from, fast? He thought of everyone he knew who would be nearby and he could only think of the guys at Chris's, and they wouldn't be any help.

"It's no good keeping things all pent up in there," the woman said. "I know that from experience."

And thinking of a car made him think of Amy and Tyler, sitting in his stolen truck, laughing their way up Route 9. Maybe the Parkway now. She picks up the kid's hand and drops it onto the edge of her pink shorts.

"If you keep things all pent up, then they get all out of proportion and things happen that don't need to happen."

How long would it take him to walk to the hospital? Could he hitch? Nobody picks up hitchhikers anymore. Especially a big guy who probably looks like he could kill somebody. And what was this song on the jukebox?

"Yep. Best to just get it all out there."

He looked down. His glass was empty.

"Don't you think so, um, I don't think I got your name."

The jukebox was playing a song he didn't even know was on it, which was saying something. Eddie had an encyclopedic knowledge of rock—he was a drywall hanger and never worked without music— plus he knew this jukebox like he knew his own mind, or at least he thought so, but this was what, some Bonnie-Raitt-ain't-it-sexy-when-we-share-our-feelings crap. Eddie stood up. He'd walk to the goddamn hospital if he had to. But they don't let you drink at the hospital. Well, there was a liquor store a few blocks away. He'd buy a pint of Jack Daniels and do it on his walk to the hospital. He got up from the table. He started for the door, and he heard the plonk. He stopped. He said, very quietly, "I didn't ask for another shot."

"This one's on me," she said. "You seem like you really need to…"

Amy starts to undo the buttons on the blouse with the little flowers while she drives. Tyler sits there and leers. Eddie's brain filled up with bricks. They pushed on the backs of his eyes. She wanted him to talk. He turned on her and started screaming. He had plans, he screamed. They woke up and they had a shower together and he had plans. The diner, and the zoo. She liked animals. She was nice, and he thought she might be the one. He stopped at the gas station, to use the men's room like a good fucking boyfriend. He was gone three minutes. And while he sat there in that smelly filthy men's room for three minutes she had herself a conversation with the college boy pumping gas, and then the fucking college boy took off his fucking clothes and got in his fucking truck, with his fucking girlfriend, and they just took the fuck off. Like it was their fucking world and fuck you Eddie.

The woman stood there with her mouth dropped open. She was staring at the blue cloth that was tossed over the bar, near the shot that she just poured. Jesus Christ he brought those goddamn coveralls with him from the gas station. There were dark streaks on them—blood from Chris Caldwell's face. Eddie reached out and grabbed the coveralls and snapped them to the floor so she couldn't see them anymore. Then he grabbed the shot, tossed it down his throat, and smacked the glass back down on the bar. He waited for the warmth, and then the detonation. He would stay here and drink and wait for Dave. How long could it take to stitch up a bad cut, a couple hours? He told the woman to draw him another Sam Adams.

She got a clean glass and went to the tap.

"Wow," the woman said quietly.

Kaboom. The walls in his head shook and dust fell. Fucking right, wow. He wondered if she was glad that he took her advice and *got it all out there*. Well this was his place, not hers, and he had to claim it if he was going to stay. Bonnie Raitt had stopped her bullshit and the bar was silent but that couldn't stand.

Eddie decided to send a message by exercising one of his privileges as Dave's best buddy. He strode to the end of the bar and reached around and beneath it. Without looking he found the small key on its hook and took it. He strode back across the room to the jukebox.

Dave's dad bought the Wurlitzer in the late seventies or early eighties, and it looked like something you'd have seen on the bridge of the original Starship Enterprise, with its rows of silver control buttons, glowing orange digits and swirling tracer lights. On one side of it were a key hole and a drawer-like thing, and he used the key to pull out the coin box. He pried a fistful of quarters out of the box and closed it again. He stood in front of the jukebox but could have made his selections without looking at it. Dave, very deliberately, stopped putting new tunes into it when he took over the bar, and so the playlist was exactly what it was in 1990. Eddie made enough selections to keep the thing going for a good half hour. He crossed the room again, watching the woman watching him, and replaced the key on its hook. She had set down his beer. He pulled out his wallet, took a twenty and slapped it down on the bar. He said, "That's for the last shot too. And the next one."

His brain was starting to loosen up. He took the beer and headed back to the table near the jukebox—no. This was his place, not hers. He would claim his regular stool near the end of the bar.

He liked this stool because it was near the wall and as far as possible from the TV, which he never looked at when he was here unless there was a good game on and everybody was watching. It was off now, and that was perfect. The first song started to play. There were three parts to talking to Dave. One of them was Dave and one of them was drinking and the third was Bruce. There was a lot of Springsteen in that Wurlitzer, including all the big rocking-out tunes, although the records had gotten so much play over the years that a lot of them didn't play right anymore. But it was the ballads—those sad, injured love songs—that got Eddie through shit, and those records played just fine because he was about the only one who liked to hear ballads in a bar.

The woman was still standing back there, watching him. She was wearing blue jeans, and a plaid shirt with the tails tied in a knot at her navel like a television hillbilly girl. The yellowish light directly above her head wasn't doing her any favors. She might even have been a few years older than him. He looked away and drank his beer. The two worked together, the bourbon and the beer, and to do it right you had to have both in just the right rhythm. It was like tearing down a building. The shots were dynamite, big loud charges at regular intervals, blasting the walls and ripping them down. The beer was the steam shovel, quietly and continually at work, chugging away, clearing the wreckage. Eddie intended to be a vacant lot by the time Dave came back to talk to him.

Bruce sang out, with his sad, worn voice. Amy's driving up the Parkway with her blouse open. Her bra is pale pink and delicate.

"You poor guy," the woman said. "I'm so sorry."

He shot a look in her direction that said, *I didn't*

catch what you said just now but it seems to be preventing you from pouring that shot I asked for. She turned and took the bottle from the back bar.

"I know what it's like," she said carefully, "to be abandoned right out of the blue like that. I know the pain you're in."

Nobody knows this pain, Eddie thought.

"I truly do," she went on. She'd poured the shot but instead of sliding it down to his end of the bar she took it and walked away, to the other end, and then around the bar to come around to his side. He didn't look up but he could follow the sound of her footsteps. She walked the full length of the bar again, and finally set the shot down in front of him.

"The same thing just happened to me," she said.

And she sat herself down on the stool next to him. Facing him.

"Just this morning."

Jesus. Eddie wrapped both hands around the glass and his brain around the song, and it wasn't easy because she was right there yammering away about some damn thing or other that happened to her and Bruce was half the room away. The song was about a guy who wanted a woman who was wary of him. She'd probably been through some bad stuff with men. He wanted to say to her that he knows love is hard but he's stronger than those other guys. Because he went through some bad stuff too. The woman slid off the bar stool and ran off to another part of the room. Score. There are so many places along the Parkway where you can pull over for a quick fuck. The County Park, right there by the zoo. Stretches of pine woods everywhere. The goddamned Oceanview Service Plaza if you can't stop yourself. The back seat of his truck. The woman was back on the stool next to him. There was something on her lap. She hadn't stopped talking the whole time. Now there was something in her hand, a small blue something, and she was trying to get him to look at it. He grabbed shot number three and tossed it back. When his head came back down the little blue thing was right there in his face. It was a Post-It note. There was handwriting on it.

Kaboom. The Jack found its mark and part of a wall fell away.

The handwriting came into focus.

Why didn't you let me shoot hoops with Bruce?

What? Eddie actually turned and looked at her. This plays basketball with Springsteen?

She'd stopped talking and was just watching him with some weird look on her face. He tried to remember if he heard any of the last couple of things she said.

The Post-It message is in Kevin's handwriting. Who's Kevin?

There was a sandy rectangle with a border of weeds and the Post-It was on the water hookup.

There was a car that was gone too. She has a twenty-minute drive to work but Kevin walks so there's only one car. The car must have been hitched to the trailer.

Trailer?

There was a trailer. But it was gone when she got back from the Walgreens with the coffee.

She only bought a can of Folgers and it was early Saturday morning so there was nobody in the checkout line.

The Walgreens was just a two-minute walk.

She walked to the Walgreens from the trailer.

She took the bag that had her wallet in it.

She put on these clothes.

She got up early to go to the Walgreens because they were out of coffee and she wanted to get back with the coffee before Kevin was out of bed.

Usually they both sleep in on Saturday morning.

They live in Sandy Pines Village.

Sandy Pines Village is a mobile home community outside Lewes.

Lewes, Delaware.

Kevin is her husband.

Okay. Some other Bruce.

The thing on her lap was the shoulder bag. It was open and there was a can of Folgers inside. She rested her hands on the bag, holding the blue Post-It between them. Eddie turned back to his beer.

She started talking again. She sounded like she'd left her body.

"I stood there and I didn't know what to do. Kevin was gone and everything was gone. I have the clothes I'm wearing. And I have what's in my bag. I don't have anyone but Kevin. Where do I go? It didn't seem to matter. I left the rectangle. And I started off down the street. I left Sandy Pines Village and I walked into Lewes. I walked through Lewes and I came to the ferry terminal. I bought a ticket for the ferry and I got on it. I rode the ferry and then I got off the ferry and I walked some more. I came to this street and then to this building and I saw a sign in the window for help wanted and it said Dave's and it was open and so I came in and I met Dave. I have bartending and serving experience."

The ferry carried cars and people across the Delaware Bay, between the southernmost tip of New Jersey and Delaware. The terminal on the Jersey side was at the end of this town, North Cape May, not Cape May proper, which was overrun by fancy people back in the seventies. North Cape May was still mostly the home of regular working people who'd been here for years, all their lives, people like Eddie and Dave. And Chris Caldwell. And Amy. And Tyler.

"So I guess I need the job." She rubbed the Post-It note. "Bruce is Kevin's buddy. They shoot hoops together."

Shit. What if they didn't drive up the Parkway? What if they went the other way and took his truck on the ferry and left the state and went to Delaware?

Her face was suddenly closer to his. "You have to do something," she said. "You have to figure out what went wrong and do something about it."

They're the first ones onto the ferry, and Amy pulls the Ram into a space right up at the bow, where nothing but a long rubber fence stands between the deck and the water. Now she hops out of the truck and twirls in the sunshine to the rubber fence. She turns and leans back against it. The unbuttoned blouse falls away to her sides and the delicate pale pink bra and its two large pink inhabitants jut out into the sunshine. She breathes in the sea air deeply. Tyler's stuck inside the truck because he has no clothes. He watches her painfully. She laughs at his longing. He likes that. Eddie's beer glass was empty again. He jabbed a finger at the beer glass and then at the shot glass.

"I'm serious," she said, and jumped up. She kept talking as she and her purse made their way back behind the bar. "Why didn't we see it coming? I didn't, and I still don't know what the hell happened. *Why didn't you let me shoot hoops with Bruce?* What is that? We have to think."

The next song was up. Bruce was singing with weary regret about a relationship that was all but done.

"Something happened last night," she said, pulling on the Sam Adams tap. "But I can barely remember last night because I could swear to you on a stack of bibles that it was a normal Friday night. We always go to the Bob Evans near Sandy Pines on Friday night. We came home from work and we went to the Bob Evans like we always do."

Eddie tried to bear down on the music. Bruce didn't want to do it, but he was ready to give up, surrender, pack it in with this woman he loved so much.

"Kevin had the country-fried steak and I had the grilled chicken. I usually have the meat loaf and gravy but I put on a few around Easter time and bathing suit weather's just around the corner, isn't it. And we talked."

They're off the ferry now. They're back in the truck and in Delaware, in Lewes. Amy's still driving.

Her face is flushed and Tyler's getting restless, his knees bouncing. Instead of continuing on Route 9 Amy makes a quick left turn and grins.

She set his beer in front of him and went for the Jack Daniels.

"Well *I* talked. Kevin's not much of a talker." She brought the bottle and plonked it down on the bar. "But that's normal too. That's not unusual. I ask him questions about his day and try to get him to tell me how he's feeling about stuff, and he gives me short little answers and that's just how he is. There was nothing special about last night."

She drives into the big state park at Cape Henlopen. On a beautiful morning before beach season there will be so many isolated places there. Tyler's thinking the same thing.

She refilled his shot glass. "Then we went home and that was the same as always too. Well he did say when we got back that he wanted to go shoot hoops with Bruce."

Bruce was in such dark pain.

"But listen, that's not unusual either. Kevin and Bruce love to shoot hoops. There's a public basketball court not too far a drive away that has lights on in the evening, and a lot of the time they go there after dinner because there's hardly ever a wait."

She's parking the truck on the nearly deserted lot. No people to be seen. He gets out, no clothes and all, runs around to her side, and opens the door for her. He offers his hand and she descends from the Ram like a queen, her eyes descending the length of him.

"But see they don't go there on Friday much so I

asked Kevin to stay home with me so we could talk some more—it seems like we never have enough time to just communicate any more, you know?"

Eddie needed to step this up—the steam shovel didn't have enough to do. He downed his shot, plonked down the glass and pointed at it as he felt the bourbon burn down through his throat.

"Already?" she asked. He said nothing. "Okay. But anyway, yeah, I guess that was a little unusual because it was Friday and I didn't want him to go, but still. Him and Bruce probably just BS about sports and bitch about work every time, so it's not like he'd be missing anything."

Kaboom. The walls shook and some cracks formed but nothing fell.

"So yeah, I asked him to stay home with me, and he did. He turned on the TV to some cop show like he always does and I try to make conversation and he watches his cop show."

The next dynamite blast was in front of him. He stared it down and took a good pull at his beer.

"And then we went to sleep."

It hurts so bad to just give up, Bruce said.

"But still," she said.

They're on a long, deserted beach. Blue sky, white sand, pine woods, crashing waves. Her sandals and his sneakers and socks are lying far behind them in the sand. She dances ahead of him, dropping the blouse with the little flowers from her shoulders, from her arms. It blows away.

"So, see?" She brought her face closer. "I still don't know what your name is."

He opened his mouth, picked up the shot glass and pitched the liquor down his throat without even touching the glass to his lips.

"Sounds like you didn't know this Amy as well as you thought you did. And that's a communication thing."

He plonked the glass down on the bar and pointed at it.

"A good relationship is based on truly knowing the other person. And you can't do that if you never talk."

She's stripping for him. Her hair in the sunlight is like an angel's. The delicate bra falls away. She slips open the top of her pink shorts. Tyler stands and watches, pitching a tent in the front of his tighty-whities.

"Did you and Amy talk?"

As a tease for Eddie (and it worked) she hadn't put on panties that morning, and so she stands there now, all pink and naked in the sun. Tyler can now see that she isn't a real blond but that only makes the tent pitch higher.

"Really talk?"

He sent down the new shot.

Amy laughs and saunters toward Tyler. He stands and waits for her.

"Ask yourself that."

She stands inches from his nose. Her nipples knot in the breeze. He waits for her. She descends to her knees, she takes the waistband of his white briefs into both hands and so slowly she rolls them down to his ankles. He steps out of them, bringing himself so close to her breath, and she tosses them to the breeze and they fly away. She watches his bobbing boner for a while and then she smiles at it, she brings out her tongue, and she drags only the curled, wet tip of it gently along the underside. She gave exactly that to Eddie in the shower this morning.

"Did you really talk? Really? Really and truly ask yourself that."

Kaboom.

The blast rocked the walls and the foundation rocked and the walls heaved and more cracks formed, but again nothing came down and the steam shovel stood there, idling. Eddie looked at the woman. He shouted, "You are not listening to me!" He slid off the stool and a hand knocked into his beer and the glass fell off the front of the bar and crashed to the floor. He reached down toward it and he must have slipped in the beer because he fell backward and hit the floor on his back. He flipped over so he could use his arms to get up but now he was all tangled up in what, shit, those goddamn coveralls. Eddie started screaming without making words. Tyler was trying to kill him. He was wrapped around his arms, his legs, his neck, choking off his air. Eddie fought. Hard. He kept screaming. He got one arm free and then another. He pulled hard and tore the coveralls away. There was a big chunk of broken glass nearby and Eddie grabbed it. Screaming, he hurled the coveralls to the floor, held them down with his free hand and drove the broken glass into them where the hairless chest would be. He dragged his hand downward, carving his way down through the torso to the groin. He returned to the chest and tore down through again.

And then again.

And again.

He felt different and he realized that a good-size chunk of the building had come down. He wasn't screaming anymore. He knelt there for a while, catching his breath. He got off his knees and used a bar stool to stand up. He looked around. Pieces of ripped-up fabric and glass and puddles of beer. The shot glass empty on top of the bar. Bruce in quiet mourning. The woman clear across the room, shrunk back against the wall. She was staring at him and she was afraid.

Shit. He never in his whole life hit a woman. He never even wanted to, ever. He loved women. Loved them too much.

"Christ," he said. "Don't. It's okay."

She didn't move.

"Here," he said. He pulled out a stool. "Have a seat. I'll get you a beer."

"I can't," she said softly. "I'm working."

Eddie felt his eyes roll. "Right. I'll get *me* a beer. It's okay. Do it all the time. Dave's my best friend."

He had to pass near her to get around the bar and she didn't move until he did that. By the time he got a clean glass she was on the floor, mopping up the beer with the coverall remains and gathering up the glass.

"That doesn't matter," he said.

"I can't have Dave coming back and seeing this," she said wearily. "I'm trying to make an impression."

"Right. Right."

He drew himself a beer and poured a shot. He

left the Jack Daniels bottle next to it. He went back around the bar and she was just standing there, the wet rags and glass in her arms. Her eyes were squeezed shut. Shit. He hated that.

"Come on," he said. He took the pile of crap away from her and found the trash basket. When he got back to her she was still standing there like that and so he led her to the stool next to his and gently pushed her onto it. He sat down. He took a swallow of his beer and looked at her. It was getting hard to keep things still but he could focus when he tried. She wasn't exactly crying but her eyes were wet.

He said, "I guess we both got fucked over pretty bad."

She hesitated for a second and then nodded a little. On this side of the bar the light seemed to treat her better. She had fewer lines on her face than he thought she had and her skin was clear. She wasn't wearing any makeup and she looked kind of pretty without it.

Bruce had just started another song. The title said it all. *I'm on Fire.*

"That's' right," Eddie said. "Let's just sit here and take it easy on ourselves."

Bruce's guitar was easy and hypnotic. Tyler's inside Amy now. They're rolling around in the sand like a tangle of snakes. Forty-two years old and he never had a woman that lasted more than a year. Dumped fourteen times. Count 'em. Eddie snatched his shot glass and tried to keep the woman from bouncing around in his vision. What was her name? Donna, right?

"I'm Eddie," he said.

She looked at him and smiled a little. It was a pretty little smile. Right, Donna. She said that. Her friends called her Don.

"Can I call you Don?"

"Sure," she said.

Eddie smiled back. With her sandy hair tied back and that knot in her plaid shirt showing some of her belly she looked a little younger than he'd thought. Somehow too her jeans were fitting her better now. He went back to her face, and brought the shot glass to his lips.

"You and me deserve a break," he said. He tilted the glass toward her as a toast, and then tilted it back again and let the Jack roll down his throat. He waited for it to hit bottom.

"Yes indeed," he said. "I got fucked over real bad. And so did you."

Kaboom. Walls came down.

"The world," he told her, "is not kind to people who just got fucked over. I'm here to tell you. But here we are. The unkind world is out there. Out there. And we're here. And we can be kind here. We can be kind here together. We can be kind to each other. And that's what we need. That's what we need. You and me." When he had a pretty woman and liquor in, the right combination the words just poured out.

She let out a shy little laugh. But her eyes were still wet. She needed to forget. He needed to forget. He put his hand on hers and she didn't move hers away.

They listened to Bruce and didn't speak. Bruce was in heat and oh, so gentle.

Eddie was the best drywall guy in Cape May County. Everybody said so. He had extraordinarily sensitive fingertips, infinite patience and a true devotion, and he worked a seam like nobody else. By the time, over the course of days, that the tape and then each micro-thin layer of joint compound had been applied, extended, dried, sanded and smoothed, there was no sign, no matter how closely you looked, that the wall had ever not been one. And women always noticed this in him. So with a true love of waiting and his extraordinarily sensitive fingers he would smooth and join and cover and sand back and smooth again, and again, until neither she nor he could tell where she ended and he began. Like they had never not been one.

People don't associate Bruce with dancing much but he doesn't have a single song that doesn't make you want to move somehow. Eddie took her hand and stood. "Don?" he asked. After a moment she stood, too. He led her, unsteadily, to the open floor and then turned to her. The knot in her shirt made a tidy package of her breasts. She let him put his arms around her waist, and then on her back. She was just the height that he liked and he slumped a little and rested his chin on her shoulder. He felt steadier. She smelled a little of sweat but he liked the actual smell of a woman better than perfume. She felt real nice in his arms.

He sang softly along with Bruce.

Eddie wanted one woman, just one, for good. He always had. The first time he felt like yeah, this is the one, it was Stephanie and he was twenty-two and he had *Steph* tattooed inside a heart over his own heart. And when she dumped him the pain was unbelievable and then there was the pain of having the tattoo removed. He swore then that he'd never get another tattoo until he found the one woman who would be his for good. And now he was forty-two and he wanted a tat like crazy and his skin was clear.

Maybe. Don's been through it too, so maybe.

They weren't dancing but they were swaying gently together which was better. His fingertips danced up and down her back and he felt like he was floating. He nestled his mouth into the curve of her neck and he kissed it. This was the first application, the first layer.

She drew in breath and stopped swaying. He kissed her neck again.

"We can't," she said. He kissed her neck again. She said, more carefully, "We can't."

He chuckled into her neck. "We are."

"No." She pulled away. He'd been using her neck to hold his head up and he almost fell. She grabbed his arm but then dropped it when he was steady. "I'm married. You have a girlfriend. They might come back. Or not. We'll have to deal with that."

Jesus. Isn't that what they're doing right now? Dealing with it?

"What's the matter? You don't like me?"

"Sure, I like you. That's not the point."

Fuck fuck *fuck*, not again. "So," he said.

"We can't."

Christ. "Why not?" He felt walls moving back in. "'Cause Amy ran off there's something wrong with me? I'm not good enough for you either?"

"I want to help you. This won't help."

"Fuck. What do you think's the matter with me?"

She just stood there. Twice in one day? Fucking Christ. He didn't want her now. He needed a blast of dynamite. He weaved his way to the bar and grabbed the bottle of Jack. He missed the glass and it splashed all over before he got some to go in.

She said, "I just wanted to help you."

"You just did shit," he said with his back to her. "You don't want to be a woman and you're a lousy fucking bartender." He closed his eyes because it made him steadier, brought the shot to his lips and drank it down.

She was crying now. "What did I do wrong?"

He slammed the glass down.

"In the first fucking place," he shouted to the back bar, "why didn't you let me go talk with Dave?"

And just like that she stopped crying and went silent. He found her reflection in the back bar's mirror and she was staring at him. Just standing and staring.

Fuck it. He shut his eyes, leaned on the bar with both arms and waited for the blast. Bruce was on to something else now. Eddie loved this song. It was long, it went on forever, and it was almost nothing but some guy crying about how much he needs his woman.

His beer was empty. He should go around and draw another one but wait, here she was and she took his glass. She took it to the tap.

She said from there, "Don't you think I know what that little cunt did to you?"

What? He looked over at her. Something was

different. The knot was undone and her shirt tails were just hanging there outside her jeans.

Wait. Did she just call Amy a cunt?

"What?" he said.

Kaboom.

"You heard me,' she said. "I know how that little cunt fucked you over."

Just the foundation was left, and that shook, hard.

He mumbled, "You don't know shit."

She walked toward him with the beer. He had to squint one eye so there weren't two of her.

"Buddy, it's these women," she said. "You have to have 'em and you think you know 'em." She set the beer down in front of him. "And the minute you think you know her, she turns around and does some shit or says some shit and you know you never did know her at all."

"Yeah, well, so," he said.

"Every time, am I right? You don't know her. You never will know her. And all the same you open yourself up and you love her and *she* knows *you*. And you just let the bitch wrap her fingers around your balls and hold tight and drag you around wherever the hell she wants to take you." She refilled the shot glass.

"Yeah," he mumbled.

"You just let her. For as long as she feels like it." She was in his face. He climbed up onto his seat and when he was steady enough he placed his thumb and fingers around the shot glass. "Until she gets bored. Or pissed off. Or just decides she's done with you."

He focused hard on the glass. He lifted it slowly until it found his lips.

"And then she lets go of your balls just like that and it's fuck you Eddie and she's gone. Just like that."

He drank the shot down.

"And you know you're gonna do the whole thing all over again next time. Over and over."

He nodded.

"Am I right, my friend?"

He nodded harder.

Bruce was begging now.

Kaboom.

"Am I right?"

It all crashed down. The tears came.

"Yes!" Eddie croaked. "Fuck yes! That's what they do!"

"Women," Don says.

"Fucking women," Eddie said.

"Fucking women." Don grabs a rag and, walking off a ways, starts to wipe down the surface of the bar.

"There is nothing you can do," Eddie shouted, "when they pull some shit."

"They got us by the balls," Don agrees.

"And they know it," Eddie shouted.

"Oh man, they know it."

"And you know what it is?" Eddie cried. It just now came together in his head. "We need 'em! And they don't need us! And we need *one* of 'em! *That's* what the fuck of it is. We need *one* of 'em!"

"I'm with you, buddy," Don says.

"If you could just let your dick drag you around through life that would be okay. You could still be your own man. But that ain't so. No, sir, that ain't possible. It's your fucking heart that drags you around."

Don chuckles. "And they know it, don't they buddy."

Eddie wrapped his fists around the beer. "Fuck yes they know it. They're fucking born knowing it." He looked down the length of the bar. This new guy with the ponytail was okay.

Don shakes his head wearily. "They got us and they know it."

"Then they're gone." Eddie tried to blink the tears away. "But fuck, you know, she's still got a hold of your heart but she's all gone away, and you're just, I don't know, what…"

Don stops wiping and looks down the bar at Eddie.

"Lost?" he says.

It felt like a rock in Eddie's throat. He gulped to clear it. "That's it, bud. You got it. You're just fucking lost." He gave in and wept.

"Women," Don says.

"Fucking women."

"What can you do."

Bruce cried and cried.

Eddie cried too. He could now. Don was okay and Don would get him though this. "You know what, bud? You know? Men are tragic figures."

"Yeah?"

"Yeah. *Yeah*. Slaves and tragic figures. Every single damn one of us."

Don drops his eight protective elbows down onto the bar. "Eddie, I think you nailed it man."

Bruce cried. It hurt so bad.

Eddie nodded, hard, and his tears splashed onto the bar, into his beer. "Tragic figures, my friend," he shouted. "Every damn one of us."

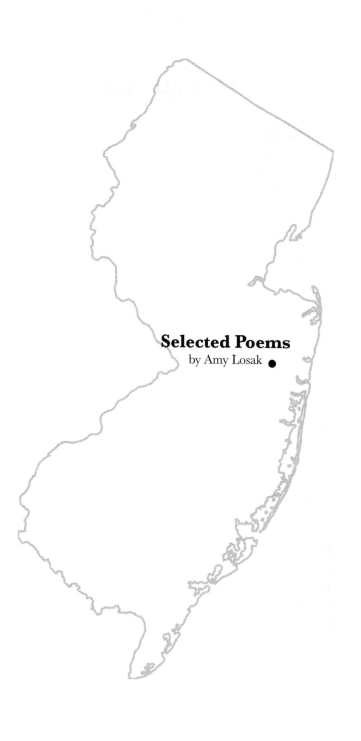

Selected Poems
by Amy Losak

HAPPY FOURTH

Morning after
the fireworks
the backyard
sparkles with
birdsong

and squirrel
grunts

and the
sun-shadowed
browns of
tree bark.

A deer
reaches to
the sky
with her
snowy throat
for succulent
green leaves.

In the
distance I
note the
barks and
yaps of
dogs

motors
revving

phones
ringing ...

and I
ponder peace
and liberty
and justice
in suburbia.

Morning Commute

Drowning in my phone
I look out at the sky

to marvel at the streaks
of smoke and blue

and shadowy buildings
in the distance

and trees smudged with gold ...

and I realize ...

this is what is real.

Morning Commute 2
(or Urban Rebirth)

Orange cranes
stab the sky.

The city sheds a
shard of its soul.

But with each
razing and
each raising

it builds
a new one.

The Tuesday Headliner ●

Story by Adam Wilson

Art by Debora Lancianese

Stay Salty Contributors

Samantha Atzeni

Samantha Atzeni is a New Jersey native and a writer of prose, comics, and academic scholarship. They graduated from The College of New Jersey with a B.A. in Professional Writing and a M.A. in English. They have written for Bustle and Sequart and have presented their work at Mid-Atalntic Popular and American Culture Association and The Faculty of the Future conferences. Samantha is co-author of the ongoing graphic novel series *The M.O.T.H.E.R. Principle* and has written two One 'n Dones for Read Furiously: *The Legend of Dave Bradley* and *Breathe*.

When Samantha isn't writing, they are a part-time professor at The College of New Jersey, teaching deconstruction theory, Holocaust and genocide studies, and sequential art theory. Samantha lives with their husband Adam Wilson, the other half of Read Furiously, their son, and their cat Alaska, who has yet to become Internet famous despite their best efforts.

Find Samantha online at
satzeni.com
instagram.com/smatzeni

Apara Mahal Sylvester

Living in Somerset County New Jersey with her husband and cats, Apara is an avid author and freelance writer. Her debut book, *Angel Child*, was her memoir. A subsequent memoir is *Chaplaincy: A Hospital Chaplain Intern's Journey*.

Apara since became inspired to write children's books. *Down By The River Where Dreams Come True*, her first children's book, is based on her love of her own cats, Babe and Boo Boo, and cats everywhere. Her other children's books are: *Cranky Frankie and The Lost Duck, Charlie The Baseball Cat, Lucy's Way Home, The Angel Tree, The Tale of Kitten and John's Best Day Ever.* Upcoming titles include: *Me and Only Me, Think of Me, To My Dear Child, Tiger the Junkyard Cat and Vinnie and the Lost Lugnut.*

Find Apara online at
aparamahalsylvester.com
instagram.com/aparamahal
facebook.com/aparamahalsylvester

Peter T. Donahue
A lifelong New Jersey resident, Peter T. Donahue has been teaching creative writing to teens for over a decade. His poetry has appeared in *The Lyric, America Magazine, Verdad, U.S. 1 Worksheets,* and *Exit 13 Magazine.*

Find Peter online at
petertdonahue.com
twitter.com/petertdonahue

Cathy Hailey
Cathy Hailey teaches as an adjunct in Johns Hopkins University's MA in Teaching Writing program and previously taught high school for forty years in Prince William County, VA. She is Northern Region Vice President of The Poetry Society of Virginia and organizes In the Company of Laureates, a reading of poets laureate held in PWC. Her poems were published in *The New*

Verse News, Poetry Virginia, Written in Arlington, NOVA Bards, Confetti, The Prince William Poetry Review, and in small anthologies associated with special projects—usually ekphrastic collections. Poems are forthcoming in *Stay Salty: Life in the Garden State, Volume 2.*

Find Cathy online at
twitter.com/haileycp
instagram.com/haileycp

Tina Scott Lassiter

Tina Scott Lassiter, MBA is an accomplished author, artist, photographer, speaker, and holistic health practitioner. Her essays, in response to current events/ issues and as reflections on daily existence, are featured on *Midnight & Indigo* and *Solstice Literary Magazines, the International Women's Writing Guild,* and BSW Chronicles websites. A former Adjunct Professor of Creative Writing for LaGuardia Community College in New York, she self-published her first book, *Morsels of Peeps,* in 2018; blogged for over 10 years; served as Art Editor/Columnist for an aspiring multicultural arts magazine in NYC; and co-edited her campus literary magazine at Howard University.

Find Tina online at
tinascottlassiter.com
instagram.com/tinascottlassiter

Shannon Linder

I have feelings full of words that I don't know how to say, so I take pictures.

My main interest lies in self-portraiture on analog film.

Sometimes I don't feel real, so I take pictures to remind myself that I am. These images bring me a sense of relief and of reassurance. The world is a concrete thing, but blurs with my daydreams more often than not. I like to create my own little world, and you can have a peek, if you like.

Find Shannon online at
shannonlinder.com
instagram.com/shannonsonfire
twitter.com/shannnonl

Elizabeth Hays Gatti

A lifelong poet, in 1994 Betsy's "Men and Their Poetry", appeared in the American Ex-POW Bulletin, and in 1995, "Yes, James," a tribute to James Baldwin, received third place in the Allen Ginsberg Poetry Awards and appeared in the *Paterson Literary Review*, as did "Beyond the Breakers" in the 2011-12 issue. In 1997, "The Face of Evil," was also published in the *Ex-POW Bulletin*. Betsy's father, Edwin W. "Red" Hays, a tail gunner on a B-17, was the inspiration. Betsy's poems have received honorable mention from the National League of Pen Women, Writer's Digest, and Theatre Guild of New Jersey.

Jill Ocone

Jill Ocone is a senior writer and editor for *Jersey Shore Magazine* and *Jersey Shore Publications* annual guidebooks. Her work has been published in *Straightening Her Crown* anthology, *Bloom Literary Magazine Volume 2*, Exeter Publishing's *From the Soil* hometown anthology, Red Penguin Books' *'Tis the Season: Poems for Your Holiday Spirit*, *American Writers Review-A Literary Journal* (2020 and 2019 volumes), *Art in the Time of Covid-19, Everywhere* magazine, and *The Sun*, among others. When Jill isn't writing or teaching high school journalism, you may find her fishing with her husband or making memories with her nieces, nephews, and family.

Find Jill online at
jillocone.com
instagram.com/jillocone
twitter.com/jillocone
facebook.com/jillocone

Margaret Montet
Margaret Montet's narratives of place are combined with memoir, research, and culture. She's a college librarian and professor (she teaches Effective Speaking!) with an MFA in Creative Writing from the Pan-European Program at Cedar Crest College. Her creative nonfiction has been published in *The Bangalore Review, Clever Magazine, Dragon Poet Review, Pink Pangea, Flying South*, and other fine periodicals and anthologies. Margaret speaks frequently on colorful and quirky places, music, news literacy, and information-seeking. Her collection of travel essays, *Nerd Traveler* (published by Read Furiously), was born in July 2021.

Find Margaret online at
margaretmontet.com
twitter.com/margaretmontet

Elizabeth Edelglass
Elizabeth Edelglass is a fiction writer and book reviewer living in Connecticut. Her short fiction has won the

Reynolds Price Fiction Prize, The William Saroyan Centennial Prize, the Lilith short story contest, and the Lawrence Foundation Prize from Michigan Quarterly Review. During this past year of isolation, she has turned to writing poetry, often finding herself drawn back to her New Jersey roots. Her poetry has appeared or is forthcoming in *Compressed, Global Poemic, Trouvaille Review, Writers Resist,* and *Sylvia.*

Find Elizabeth online at
instagram.com/elizabeth.edelglass
twitter.com/lizedelglass

Patrick Lombardi

Patrick Lombardi was born and raised in New Jersey and currently resides in Mercer County. He graduated from Rider University, with a bachelor's degree in English. He is a full-time employee with the state and contributes to BestofNJ.com. He also has been published in outlets such as Buzzfeed, NJ.com, The Times of Trenton, Odyssey, MyCentralJersey.com, Courier News, Home News Tribune, and Patch.com. His first book, *Junk Sale,* a collection of humorous short stories and essays, was published in August 2018.

Find Patrick online at
patricklombardi.com
instagram.com/patlombardi4
facebook.com/PatrickLombardiWriter
twitter.com/patlombardi4

GR Lear

G.R. Lear is a NJ cartoonist who grew up reading

comics in the Garden State. He works in both traditional and digital mediums to create stories of exploration and wonder. He runs educational workshops and self-publishes his work under the moniker Unlimited Wonder Comics.

Find GR online at
unlimitedwondercomics.com
instagram.com/unlimitedwondercomics
twitter.com/unlimitedwonder

A.J. Pellegrino
Alyce has worked in academic publishing for the last five years and has a B.A. in Creative Writing from Purchase College. She is currently living in New Jersey.

Find A.J. online at
alycepellegrino.com
instagram.com/aprilsteahouse
twitter.com/aprilsteahouse

Kathy Kremins
Kathy Kremins is a Newark, NJ native of Irish immigrant parents and a retired public school teacher. She is the author of *The Ethics of Reading: The Broken Beauties of Toni Morrison, Arundhati Roy, and Nawal el Sadaawi*, and a book of poetry, *Undressing the World*, forthcoming from Finishing Line Press in June 2022. Kathy's work appears in *The Night Heron Barks, The Paterson Literary Review*, Moving Words 2020 project, *The Stillwater Review, Lavender Review, Sensations Magazine, Divine Feminist: An Anthology of Poetry & Art By Womxn and Non-Binary Folx*, and *Too Smart to be Sentimental: Contemporary Irish American Women Writers*.

Find Kathy online at
instagram.com/kreminsk
twitter.com/kathykremins

Scott Napp

Scott Napp is proudly a shore native. After graduating from The College of New Jersey, he went for broke producing a Garden State-set comedic web series. "Issues" helped him gain membership in the Writers Guild of America at 25. His love for Cape May's deep history and rich local legends led to the creation of "Off Season." By day, he is the video production teacher for Howell High School's award-winning Fine and Performing Arts Center program. By night he develops short stories, novels and screenplays that range from space operas to horror-comedies to true crime. He lives in Central NJ (and yes, he firmly believes it exists) with his wife Jaime and their three crazy birds.

Find Scott online at
scottnap.com
instagram.com/scottnap
twitter.com/superscottnap

Jimmy Cullen

Jimmy was not born in New Jersey but was raised in Hamilton. When he graduated from Hamilton High School West he went to Drew University up in north Jersey. Afterwards, Jimmy submerged himself in the world of customer service and dabbled in education. What he has experienced throughout his life is what fuels his poetry: bullying, homosexuality, spirituality, and surviving his own suicide attempt. He suffers from Bipolar I

Disorder that causes him to have bouts of mania. Jimmy's poems are a testament to his strength and wisdom which he earned from living in Hamilton and dealing with his mental illness.

Gaveth Pitterson

Jamaican born and raised author Gaveth Pitterson now based in New Jersey, is a Wellness Coach of over fourteen years with a Career in Banking for over twenty years, Business Owner and Operator of GNP Nutrition, Certified Health and Wellness Coach and Consultant. Gaveth is passionate about serving her community and helping others live a healthy active and fulfilling lifestyle. Writing professionally and becoming an author has always been on her bucket list.

When she's not busy working she enjoys spending time with her grandsons, biking with her hubby, enjoying the outdoors, cruising and traveling around the world.

Find Gaveth online at
gumroad.com/gavethpitterson
instagram.com/gnpnutrition
facebook.com/AuthorGavethPitterson/

Eileen Moeller

Eileen Moeller lives in Philadelphia. She has an M.A. in Creative Writing from Syracuse University, and numerous publications in literary journals, such as *Sugar Mule, Philadelphia Stories, Paterson Literary Review,* and *Blue Fifth Review,* and anthologies, most recently *Fifty Over Fifty* ed. Carla Spataro for Rathalla Review. She has two books: *Firefly, Brightly Burning* Grayson Books (2015) and *The*

Girls in their Iron Shoes Finishing Line Press (2016). Her poetry collection *Silk City Sparrow* was published by Read Furiously in 2020.

Find Eileen online at
eileenmoeller.blogspot.com

Bill Hemmig

Bill Hemmig's story, "Cutthroat Alley," appears in the 2019 Read Furiously anthology, *The World Takes: Life in the Garden State*. He has had other short fiction published in the magazines *Philadelphia Stories* and *Children, Churches & Daddies*, and has twice been named a finalist, for fiction and flash fiction, in the New Millennium Writing Awards. Previous to taking on fiction writing he was the author of eight plays that were produced Off-Off-Broadway and regionally. He is also Dean of Learning Resources & Online Learning at Bucks County Community College in Pennsylvania. Bill's first novella, *Brethren Hollow*, was released as part of Read Furiously's One 'n Done series in 2020.

Find Bill online at
twitter.com/billhemmig
instagram.com/billhemmig

Amy Losak

Amy Losak has lived in New Jersey since 1998. She is healthcare public relations consultant.

Amy's mother, Sydell Rosenberg, was a teacher and published writer. Syd was a charter member of the Haiku

Society of America in 1968. Amy is a member today.

Thanks to Syd's influence, Amy writes her own poetry. This year, she won first place in HSA's annual Gerald Brady memorial senryu contest. There were more than 700 entries:

brooding
over world events
cicadas

In 2018, Penny Candy Books released *H Is For Haiku*. Amy wrote the introduction. This vibrant children's collection was honored by the National Council for Teachers of English in 2019.

In 2020, Kattywompus Press published Syd's mixed poetry chapbook for adults, *Poised Across the Sky*. In 2022, Kelsay Books will release their collaborative chapbook, *Wing Strokes Haiku*.

Find Amy online at
twitter.com/AmyLosak
linkedin.com/in/amy-losak-836b686/

Adam Wilson

A former comic editor, Adam Wilson is one of the co-publishers of Read Furiously. As a comic writer, Adam has published two graphic novels: *Brian & Bobbi* and *In the Fallout*. He co-writes the graphic novel series *The MOTHER Principle,* and his short stories have been featured in numerous anthologies. Adam is also a contributor to the Read Furiously One 'n Done series which features his first novella *What About Tuesday* and his graphic novella *Helium*. Adam lives in West Trenton with his wife, and fellow Read Furiously founder, Samantha Atzeni, and their son and cat.

Find Adam online at
lifeinasplashpage.com
instagram.com/amwilson81
twitter.com/amwilson81

Debora Lancianese

Debora Lancianese was born in 1996 in a little town in Italy where she graduated to an art school. After that she continued her studies to the International School of Comics and consecutively she has been working with little publishers.

Find Debora online at
instagram.com/debora_lancianese_
facebook.com/debora.lancianese

A Note to our Furious Readers

From all of us at Read Furiously, we hope you enjoyed *Stay Salty*, the first volume of our *Life in the Garden State* anthology series.

There are countless narratives in this world and we would like to share as many of them as possible with our Furious Readers.

It is with this in mind that we pledge to donate a portion of these book sales to causes that are special to Read Furiously and its creators. These causes are chosen with the intent to better the lives of others who are struggling to tell their own stories.

Reading is more than a passive activity – it is the opportunity to play an active role within our world. At Read Furiously, its editors and its creators wish to add an active voice to the world we all share because we believe any growth within the company is aimless if we can't also nurture positive change in our local, national, and global communities. The causes we support are designed to encourage a sense of civic responsibility associated with the act of reading. Each cause has been researched thoroughly, discussed openly, and voted upon carefully by our team of Read Furiously editors.

To find out more about who, what, why, and where Read Furiously lends its support, please visit our website at readfuriously.com/charity

Happy reading and giving, Furious Readers!

Read Often, Read Well, Read Furiously!

Be sure to check out the first volume in our New Jersey Anthology Series

Available wherever books are sold!

Look for these other great titles from

Read Often. Read Well.

<u>Poetry</u>

All These Little Stars
Silk City Sparrow
Dear Terror
Whatever you Thought, Think Again
Until the Roof Lifted Off
Chocolate Brown Satin Hot Pants and Other Artifacts
Heirlooming

<u>**Essays and Anthologies**</u>

Nerd Traveler
We don't do "just okay" anymore
Furious Lit vol 1: Tell Me A Story
The World Takes: Life in the Garden State
Putting Out: Essays on Otherness
Working Through This

CPSIA information can be obtained
at www.ICGtesting.com
Printed in the USA
BVHW040947131021
618834BV00016B/668

9 781737 175841